LAST RESORT

S.I.N. SERIES
book one

NEW YORK TIMES BESTSELLING AUTHOR

K. BROMBERG

PRAISE FOR K. BROMBERG

"K. Bromberg always delivers intelligently written, emotionally intense, sensual romance . . ."

—*USA Today*

"K. Bromberg makes you believe in the power of true love."

—#1 *New York Times* bestselling author Audrey Carlan

"A poignant and hauntingly beautiful story of survival, second chances, and the healing power of love. An absolute must-read."

—*New York Times* bestselling author Helena Hunting

"An irresistibly hot romance that stays with you long after you finish the book."

—#1 *New York Times* bestselling author Jennifer L. Armentrout

"Bromberg is a master at turning up the heat!"

—*New York Times* bestselling author Katy Evans

"Supercharged heat and full of heart. Bromberg aces it from the first page to the last."

—*New York Times* bestselling author Kylie Scott

Standalone
Faking It
Then You Happened
Flirting with 40
UnRaveled (Novella)
Sweet Cheeks
Sweet Rivalry (Novella)

The Play Hard Series
Hard to Handle
Hard to Hold
Hard to Score
Hard to Lose
Hard to Love

The S.I.N. Series
Last Resort
On One Condition
Final Proposal

Holiday Novellas
The Package
The Detour

Published by JKB Publishing, LLC

ISBN: 978-1-942832-43-0

Cover design by IndieSage
Editing by Marion Making Manuscripts
Formatting by Champagne Book Design
Printed in the United States of America

LAST RESORT

CHAPTER ONE

Sutton

"PENNY FOR YOUR THOUGHTS, SUTTON."

"What?" I ask my boss, distracted and more than a little tired.

Not exactly the best state to be in when trying to impress a new client, but *it* was definitely worth it.

Roz studies me with a quizzical expression and repeats, "I said a penny for your thoughts."

Everything from last night flashes in my mind. Him standing between my thighs. The incredible burn the first time he pushed into me.

Tell me what you want. His words whispered into the curve of my shoulder.

The grip of his hands on my thighs.

The slide of his tongue over my skin.

The feel of his cock in me.

Drowning in pleasure like I've never felt before.

I give Roz what I'm certain is a *deer in the headlights* look as I struggle with how to answer her. "I—um—"

"Don't be nervous." She offers a pat on the top of my hand, mistaking my fumbling for anxiety instead of a trip down memory lane.

"I'm not."

I am.

How do I even have the bandwidth to be nervous?

But when I look around the imposing lobby, how can I not be? I mean, we are on the top floor of a skyscraper in Manhattan waiting to meet the people who will be the judge of my skills.

Add to that, after the whirlwind of the past twenty-four hours, anxiety should be my middle name. The confrontation with my best friend, Lizzy. Roz unexpectedly selecting me to lead this project. My unanticipated breakup with Clint. My first and only one-night stand, which I'm honestly still reeling from hours after waking up in an empty bed in the hotel suite.

"You are." She offers me a smile, her eyes studying me from behind the frames of her black glasses. "Look. I know this is last minute and you're still trying to digest all the details I've thrown at you, but I have no doubt you'll do great. And what you don't know, just fake it till you figure it out." She winks. "If you're going to be thrown to the wolves, at least pretend you know how to howl. That's how we all do it."

"I'll save you from me howling right now." I chuckle and think of the client files and specs I pored over this morning as I gulped down my espresso. Let's just hope I can remember enough of the important details to sound coherent for this meeting. At least I'll have three days and a long plane ride to memorize the remainder of the specifics.

"You'll do fine. Just remember the partners aren't as intimidating as they seem at first. Plaster a smile on your lips and look at me if you need me to fill in the blanks for you."

I assume she's speaking of the Sharpe brothers of Sharpe International Network (or S.I.N. as the receptionist referred to it on the phone when we walked in), but Roz's words, now that we are standing in their office, are a complete contradiction to what she said yesterday. Yesterday she claimed the partners were consummate perfectionists, demanding yet fair. Reluctantly, I nod. That's all I can do because there's no backing out now.

"Oh, and just a warning, the three of them are—"

"They're ready for you now," a smartly dressed assistant says, her heels clicking on the white marble floors as she approaches us.

"Thank you," Roz and I both say as we stand and follow her. I study the seam of her pencil skirt in an attempt to abate the nerves rioting within me.

I can do this.

Do one thing for you, Sutton.

Lizzy's words repeat in my head, an affirmation that I'm doing the right thing, as the assistant opens the tall door into the conference room. Roz enters first with me following behind her.

"Gentlemen," Roz says in way of greeting as she steps to the side to give me a clear view of the room's occupants.

My feet falter.

My heart stops.

My jaw falls lax.

Oh. Shit.

Sitting on the opposite side of the conference table from where we stand is the man who was wrapped around me—was in me, was on me—last night. I then glance to the second man and *oh shit.* There's two of them. *Twins. Is this for real? You're just stressed. Just exhausted.* I draw in a shaky breath as I glance at the third man, returning with his coffee to the table.

Oh. Fuck.

This can't be happening.

There are *three* of them. Identical *triplets.* All three stunningly handsome. All three staring directly at me.

And I swear to God, I have no idea whose scent is still in my nose and whose taste is still on my tongue.

"Hello there," the middle one with the crisp white shirt and bold red tie says. His smile is crooked but given with a mixture of warmth and amusement. "Sorry. Did Roz not warn you? We know it can be a little jarring walking in and seeing the three of us."

"I'm sorry. Yes." *Get your wits about you.* I give a small shake of my head. "Hello." I work a swallow down my throat as I fight the heat creeping into my cheeks. "I'm Sutton Pierce." I meet each one of their eyes, my tongue thick in my mouth. I'm not sure if I want *or* don't want to see a flicker of recognition in one of them. "Nice to meet you."

The one on the right draws my eyes as he chuckles. He has a dark gray dress shirt on. It's open at the collar, his shirtsleeves rolled up showcasing firm forearms and strong hands. His hair is a little longer than his brothers'. I stare at his hands, my mind wondering if they were the ones that rendered me breathless one moment and crying out the next.

"It's our pleasure." His eyes meet mine when I look up. Hold them. *Was it him?*

Images from last night flash through my head. *Paralyze me.* Me on my knees looking up at his amber-colored eyes with his cock thick and hard on my lips. The way his teeth dug into his bottom lip as he pushed his way into me. The curl to his hair as he licked me between my thighs. The way he . . . made me *feel* when I never knew I could feel like *that.*

The snapshots are like a reel in my head.

A reel I can't stop.

I'm aroused. Confused. Dumbfounded.

So fucking screwed.

And all these things are happening as I'm standing and being judged by the men before me.

"Please, take a seat," the brother on the left says. I take in his white dress shirt, dark gray vest, and yellow tie. But he has the same eyes. The same smile. The same hair.

And he has a Starbucks to-go cup sitting in front of him.

It had to be him. *Right?*

Snap out of it. Act normal. *Act like one of these men didn't ruin you for other men.*

"Thank you," I murmur and take a seat next to Roz, blaringly aware that one of these men is currently undressing me with his eyes. It takes everything I have not to stare at each one, to try and remember his nuances so I can figure out which one I was with. Either that or crawl under the table and die from absolute mortification.

Instead, I focus more intently than any human should on getting my pad of paper and pen out of my bag so I can take notes.

"I'm Fordham Sharpe," yellow tie and vest says. "Please, call me Ford. This is Ledger." He points to the brother in the middle with the red tie. "And that's Callahan." Dark gray shirt, no tie, lifts his hand and nods.

"There will be a test later," Callahan says, drawing my eyes back to him. Our gazes hold for a beat. *Are you Johnnie Walker?*

"Don't worry," Ledger says, pulling me from my dizzying thoughts. "The longer you work with us, the more you'll be able to tell us apart. We really are quite different."

Callahan snorts.

"He's the youngest," Ford offers up and smirks as Callahan rolls his eyes. "We try not to hold that against him."

All three smile and I swear even Roz sighs beside me from the sheer beauty of the sight in front of us.

"Let's get started, shall we?"

CHAPTER TWO

Sutton

Twenty-four Hours Earlier

"TEN O'CLOCK TONIGHT. CLUB COQUETTE."

"Stepping up in the world, are we?" I tease. Club Coquette is the place to be right now, but velvet ropes are only lifted if you know someone or are someone. "How'd you score those tickets or access or whatever it is you need to get in?"

"I may or may not be dating one of the managers there."

I lift my eyebrows at something that is so Classic Lizzy. She always happens to be with the right people at the right times. She attracts good luck and good times like a magnet.

"So . . . Come with us? It'll be the first girls' night out that you can make in *forever*."

"I can't," I whisper into my phone as I pop my head above my cubicle to make sure no one can hear me from my corner in the back of the office. Or see my grimace in response to my best friend's question.

I never should have answered the call. Especially not when things have been so strained between us these past few months.

"As expected," Lizzy murmurs and emits a resigned sigh. It sounds much like how I feel these days.

"What's that supposed to mean?"

"It means when is the last time *Clingy Clint* let you out of his sight? It's a girls' night out for Christ's sake. Does he own your every waking moment?"

"Lizzy . . . That's not it."

"That *is* it, Sutton. The prick can go out and have all the fun he wants but, not shockingly, you're *not allowed* because he might suddenly need you. He can take promotions and climb the corporate ladder, and yet the minute you think about doing the same, he makes you doubt your own abilities so you turn down similar opportunities. Hell, he even helps you pick out the dresses to wear to his corporate functions, and then when you're there, he humiliates you by publicly stating how you made the wrong choice." She makes a sound that can only be akin to frustration as tears burn in my eyes.

I knew I was going to regret spilling my guts out to her last month. My call to her was a moment of frustrated weakness that is now, of course, going to be used against me.

The part of me that wants to cling to her for support gives way to my need to protect Clint and my pride.

"I'm at work. I can't have this conversation right now."

"There's always a reason you can't have the conversation. Always an excuse for him." There is a pleading in her voice that I pretend not to hear. "I mean, look at you. In your work life you kick ass on the daily, and the only thing I can gather is that it's the one part of your life he can't touch or influence."

"Lizz—"

"I don't mean to hurt you, but you simply can't see it." Her sigh is heavy when I don't respond. "I know you love him, but this isn't love. This is control with the obsession to tear you down just to build himself up."

"That's not true," I whisper without an ounce of conviction.

"He has sapped every bit of that spark and personality from my best friend, and I'm not having it anymore. I've sat idly by for the last two years and watched you slip away as he's pulled the strings that control you tighter and tighter, and I can't do it anymore. I'd rather ruin our friendship by telling you the truth than by letting you become a shadow of the person I know you to be."

"I said I can't do this right now."

And yet I don't hang up.

I don't even attempt to.

Because I know she's right. Nothing that she's said is news to me. In fact, they're things I've told myself over and over. Things I've thought about late at night when he's out, and I'm home alone. I've even gone so far as admitting to myself that our relationship is unhealthy. That our talks of marriage and a future are just that—*talks*. I know I can't do this forever and yet . . . I'm not strong enough to walk away just yet.

Or am I?

The thought sucker-punches me. The truth of it knocking the wind from me as Lizzy drones on in my ear.

Has he beaten me down that much? So much so that thoughts of how much he needs me overrides my own well-being? That his constant refrain about how he'd fall apart without me taking care of him has become more important than who is taking care of me?

And yet I repeat the company line. "Lizzy. He needs me—"

"Don't you dare sit there and think he'd be devastated without you," she starts. "He's a grown-ass man, able to take care of himself. He has manipulated you into thinking that if you ever leave him, he'll crumble. That's his problem. *Not yours*."

"It's not as easy as you think." I'm embarrassed to even utter those words because I'm in my mid-twenties and should have my life together. Lizzy's aware of my mountains of student debt but not my almost non-existent savings. There's nowhere in New York I can live on my own.

I grimace.

That's not a good enough reason to be living with Clint.

My God. Is that why I've stayed?

"I know it's not easy. In fact, I know it's harder than hell because he's stolen so much from you and conditioned you to believe that you can't do it."

"We live together. I can't just up and leave and—"

"You can, Sutt. You actually can *just up and leave*. I told you before that you're welcome to stay with me till you figure shit out. That offer is still there."

"Thank you." It's all but a whisper because her words are screaming in my head and beginning to drown out the oppressive fear that has owned me for longer than I want to admit.

It's a weird thing to know what the right thing to do is—to want to do it—but to fall victim to the guilt and shame over why you can't.

"I miss my friend who used to dance on bar tops with me and the one who'd call me to go get ice cream at three in the morning because she was working late and missed me. I miss your laughter and your sense of humor. I will never forgive him for stealing that from you. Sutt, I just miss *you*."

I cough over the sob stuck in my throat as I make a hasty exit from my office to the bathroom where I can hide to gather my composure.

"Lizz . . ." My hiccup echoes around the empty tile room as I lock the door behind me. "I'm still here. I'm still me. I'm . . ."

"And I still love you."

Her words hurt too much to hear. "I have to go."

With my back against the door, I slide down to the floor, tears flowing and emotion overwhelming me.

She's right.

She's right, and I'm terrified because is *this* moment—*right now*—the straw that breaks the camel's proverbial back?

The question is, do I want it to be?

The tears come harder as I sit unladylike on the expensive marble floor and allow myself a moment to feel sorry for myself. And then a few more to come to grips with everything Lizzy just laid out on the table.

My phone alerts a text.

Lizzy: Are you okay?

Me: I will be.

Lizzy: I love you. I only want the best for you.

I sniffle as the screen blurs through my tears. I shove them away with the back of my hand and take a deep breath. I then type the hardest question I've asked in forever.

Me: How do I do this?

Lizzy: With baby steps. You're not alone. Start with doing one thing for yourself today. Just one thing. Promise me you will.

Me: I promise.

I stare at the screen, at my promise, as my tears subside and my resolve fortifies.

One thing.

I can do that.

Baby steps.

And as I collect myself off the bathroom floor and press cold towels to my cheeks to wipe away the tears, I realize there is something potent in the notion of acceptance. That once you accept the truths you've been running from, you begin to have power over them.

"You okay?"

I give a quick glance to my cubicle partner, Melissa, and nod. "Fine. My allergies are acting up."

"You sure?" She takes a closer look, and I offer her a smile. Hiding my puffy eyes will only serve to further her suspicions.

"Yep. Happens every once in a while." I shrug as if I wasn't just bawling my eyes out while questioning my life's decisions. "What's up?"

"I was just coming to look for you. Roz wants to see you."

I do a double take. "Me? Why?"

She never wants to see associate consultants unless they are in trouble or getting fired. Did someone hear me in the bathroom? Did she see me take a personal call on company time? Am I—

"No clue, but I wouldn't keep her waiting."

Within minutes, I'm sitting in the glass palace that Resort Transition Consultants' owner, Roz, calls an office. Its floor-to-ceiling windows claim to look out over Manhattan but actually look at another skyscraper nearby. I rub my clammy hands up and down my slacks and hope to God she doesn't notice the evidence of my emotional breakdown and mistake the red eyes for drinking while on the job or something random like that.

She sits across from me in her trademark black sweater, black-framed glasses, and matching black pixie cut and studies me.

"We have a last-minute project that's come on board."

"That's great," I say. Internally I groan because we're already spread thin as it is.

"It is, especially since this client is next level for us. The commission on this project alone would be worth it, but the notoriety and reputation that we'd achieve from being a part of it is invaluable." She twists her lips, and I swear if I weren't sitting in front of her, she'd be rubbing her hands together, already counting the money rolling in. "The only downside is that we're expected to be up to speed, ready to work, and on-site in five days."

"Okay," I say just to simply participate in the conversation because, as much as we all love working for Roz, there is nothing Roz likes more than hearing herself talk.

But five days? What is this insanity?

"Our client recently purchased a property in the Virgin Islands that is floundering. It's a great location, scenic and gorgeous, but it has issues."

"As they all do."

"That's where we come in." Her grin beams. "We've been hired to come in and assess the issues so the owners can make the resort shine like the beauty it can be." *With five days to prep? Seriously?*

A resort in the Virgin Islands, though. What I'd give to have time away from normal life to devote to my work while sorting through my personal problems.

"Sounds like a great opportunity for RTC."

"You don't know the half of it." She waves a hand at me to let me know she does. "Who would turn down working in paradise for a few months? Hell, I'd take on the project if I could, but I can't leave with everything that's going on."

"So . . ." I try and gauge what she's asking me without verbalizing. "You need me to help Gwen get everything together for it since she's busy with the Rothschild's properties, then?" I ask, referring to the senior consultant I'm assigned to on most projects. And by assigned, I mean that I do all the work and she gets all the glory.

"Not this go 'round."

"Then what do you need?"

She pushes a few things around on her desk before looking back up to meet my eyes. "I know I'm wasting my time asking since you've previously told me you didn't feel prepared to take on anything more than a role as an associate, but I'm going to ask anyway. Would you be interested in this project, Sutton?"

"Of course. Like I said, I can assist any way possible."

"I know you can, but that's not what I'm asking." She smiles. "Would you like to run this project?"

I stare at her dumbfounded for a beat. "Run, run?"

"Yes. Run, run. Be the lead on it. The senior consultant in charge. The one making all the decisions with the clients."

"In the Virgin Islands?"

"That is where the project is, yes."

I clear my throat as my palms grow even more sweaty and my pulse races. "You are aware that I've never worked on a project this size let alone run one before, right?" Only projects with small budgets and low stakes. Projects that aren't an entire resort with what seems like unlimited funds or that require ten times more experience than I have. "I mean, I have no doubt I can do it and do it to our client's liking . . . but it's a huge risk putting me as lead."

"I'm aware." She nods and gives me a reassuring smile. "But I also know you have to learn sometime and maybe that time is now. There is nothing better than hands-on experience to teach you. Everything I ever learned in this business was from being pushed out of my comfort zone."

She's forgetting the part where my lack of experience would embarrass RTC if I screwed up and possibly lose us this huge opportunity working with the client would offer.

"If this client is so important, why aren't you asking one of the senior consultants to take it? I'd be happy to finish up one of their existing projects already in the works."

"Because our client has asked for a dedicated designer who will focus solely on their project and their project alone."

"In other words, they're demanding."

"When you're successful like they are, you can be anything you want to be. Why change when people would kill for the chance to have you as a reference on their portfolio?"

I stare at my boss with a million questions running through my mind. Why me? What if I fail? What if, what if, what if . . . and yet I know she wouldn't have asked me if she didn't have confidence in me and my abilities.

"And the second part of my answer," she says when my silence remains, "is that I believe in you, Sutton. Not only are you a quick study with good ideas, but I've been following your work. Gwen tells me all the time about your dedication and contributions to her projects, and I think it's time you realize your full potential. Of course, the project would come with a raise, lodging at the resort while you're there, and the potential for a promotion upon the project's completion." Our eyes meet and our gazes hold. "I'm not trying to pressure you into saying yes. The last thing I want is for you to take it on out of obligation and then be miserable because that will show in your work, but at the same time, if you keep refusing opportunities, there will be no more growth here at RTC." She offers a soft and encouraging smile as adrenaline begins to hum beneath my skin. "So, what do you say?"

Do just one thing for you today.

I recall the last time Roz asked me to step up. The mountains of excuses I made why I couldn't take it because, God forbid, I advanced quicker than Clint in his career. How he told me it was for the best that I didn't take the project and embarrass myself, the firm or, more importantly, him. And then how I cried in the shower that night so he couldn't hear, feeling like I'd let myself down, all while rationalizing it in some futile way.

I think it's time you realize your full potential.

Oh my God. How could I have done that to myself? I'm damn good at my job.

My pulse thunders in my ears, courage mounting with each beat of my heart as I look at Roz and smile. "Yes. I'm very interested . . ."

Roz startles at my unexpected words. "Really?"

I inhale a shaky breath and nod. "Yes. I'd love the opportunity." *Baby steps.* "It's terrifying but I'm more than ready."

"All good things in life should scare you a little. That's how you know you're really living."

Eighteen Hours Ago

"Sutton? Honey?" Lizzy says as she stares at me on her doorstep, bags at my feet, and a lost look on my face.

"You were right." My voice is barely a whisper as I stare at my best friend. I don't say anything else and yet she knows why I'm standing here and exactly what I need. She ushers me inside her apartment, wraps her arms around me, and just holds tight.

"It's going to be okay," she murmurs over and over in a soothing voice as we stand there. I feel like I can actually breathe for the first time in way too long. "Tell me what happened."

So I proceed to tell her about Roz's offer. About my acceptance of the job in an attempt to stay true to my word to Lizzy to do one thing for myself. And then about Clint's explosion when I got home and told him I'd taken the offer.

How at first his words were composed, even, but biting. How I thought he just needed time to warm up to the idea. Hell, I even invited him to come to the Virgin Islands with me and work remotely. But the more I insisted I was excited for the opportunity, the angrier he became. His fist through the drywall, his insults degrading, and his fury and pettiness undeniable.

And then the cool calm afterwards.

"You will never be anything without me, Sutton." His too calm demeanor is unsettling. "We both know that. But go ahead and go if you're so dead set on experiencing failure. Just remember we have dinner with my boss next Friday. So make sure you're back by then because it won't be pretty for you if you embarrass me."

"We're over, Clint," I repeat for what feels like the tenth time in as many minutes. How did I not hear these veiled threats before? Why have I always complied instead of standing up to him?

His smile is mocking. The lift of an eyebrow a challenge to how serious my words are.

My only response is to continue shoving whatever is within reach into my overnight bag. I'm too flustered, too hurt, to properly pack what I really need, but I can't hesitate. If I do, he'll pounce, with the intention to show that I don't mean what I said.

That we're not really over.

"You'll be back. There's no way you'll ever survive on your own without me holding your hand and fixing your constant mistakes." He looks me up and down and gives a disgusted shake of his head. "But be prepared to grovel." He chuckles. "There's a price to pay for realizing I'm the greatest thing that's ever happened to you."

"It was like for the first time I could see his actions clearly, I could really hear his words, but it was almost as if I was so far removed from the emotion in the moment, that I could see what you've been seeing all along," I finally say with a shake of my head. "His need for control. His need to make me less than. His need for me to fit in a box for his use only."

She just squeezes my hand and nods where we sit side by side on her couch. "So you left."

I nod. "I told him it was over. That we were done and"—I shrug— "I packed a few bags, drove around for a while, and then ended up here."

"And how do you feel now that you've had some time to think?"

I twist my lips and try to summon any emotion. I should feel something, right? I should want to scream and yell and punch something after breaking up with a man I've been with for two years, but I don't feel anything other than exhaustion. Simple and utter exhaustion.

Actually, that's a lie.

I can pinpoint one and only one emotion.

"*Relief.*" I look at my best friend and give a half-hearted smile. "I feel absolute relief, and nothing more."

"Then I guess that tells you all you need to know."

And it does.

I'm sure at some point I'll grieve the loss of something that used to be my sole focus. The loss of what? I'm not one hundred percent sure because the good memories have been so few and far between these last two years that I struggle to recall one that didn't result in me either giving up on something for him or biting my tongue for one reason or another.

I sink into the couch, lean my head back, and close my eyes to take in the moment.

A moment I've known was coming for some time but haven't had the courage to act on.

One thing is certain, I obviously disconnected from Clint long before today. Because my nonchalance isn't shock. Rather it's me doing something I know I should have done a long time ago. I read once that women leave relationships emotionally way before they leave physically. *And I just proved that theory.*

This is me reclaiming me again.

I did it.

I finally did it.

And now I already hate myself for taking so long to get here.

Fifteen Hours Ago

I stand at the bathroom doorway and watch Lizzy fuss with putting on her fake lashes. Her makeup is flawless, her hair stunning, and the tight, sparkly dress she'll be putting on any minute hangs in the corner. Its sequins create prisms of light all over the room.

"They look like a nightmare to put on," I murmur, pointing at the lashes between her fingertips.

"You get the hang of it when you do it enough." She turns and tugs on my hand to pull me into her space. "Let me put some on you."

"Kind of a waste using them on me, don't you think?"

"Then come with us and it won't be a waste," she says as she grabs both of my arms and squeezes. "I know you don't feel your best right now, but maybe some girlfriend time and cocktail therapy will help cheer you up."

"I don't know," I murmur. "Will it . . ."

"Will it what? Look bad to go out and let loose after being held back for so long?" She rolls her eyes dramatically. "Of course, it won't. People do it all the time. C'mon. Get dressed up and come with me. I have a dress that's perfect for you. And if you want to leave at any time, we can." She pulls me in for a quick hug with her one lash on and one lash off. "It's okay to want to feel alive, Sutton."

CHAPTER THREE

Sutton

Twelve Hours Ago

CLUB COQUETTE IS EVERYTHING IT ADVERTISES. SWANKY. High-end. Overwhelming. Ridiculously pretty people flit about from table to table in the VIP lounge area where Lizzy has set up court. Music plays, its bass thumping a dull throb but not overwhelming, as the dance floor is in a separate area on the other side of the bar.

The lights are dim and the conversation a low hum as people flirt, mingle, and decompress after a hard day's work.

And then there's me. A little tipsy, simply enjoying myself as I stand at the far end of the bar, waiting for the bartender so I can order another drink.

My phone vibrates in my hand, and I glance down at it with a resigned sigh. I'm not sure if I want it to be Clint—so I know that at least I'll be missed—or if I don't want it to be as a means to prove that I was right; I mean nothing to him.

"I wouldn't do that if I were you," a voice from my left says.

"*You wouldn't do what?*" I reply in reflex without looking, my attention lifting from the text I haven't read and over to *him*.

Him, as in the devastatingly handsome—devastating *everything*—man who is standing a few feet from me. I'm met with a pair of amber-colored eyes that hold amusement as he studies me. He has dark lashes, a strong jaw, and a mouth that I already know was made for sin.

I probably look like an idiot as I stare at him, mouth open and mute, while I take in his dark dress shirt and rolled-up shirtsleeves that showcase sexy forearms and strong hands.

My gaze finds its way back up his chest and broad shoulders, over his lips that break out into a half-cocked grin, to meet his eyes again. He lifts his eyebrows as if to ask me if I like what I see.

"I wouldn't answer that text," he finally responds when he knows he has my full attention.

"Why's that?" I turn to face him and lean my hip against the edge of a barstool. He's . . . *beautiful* for lack of a better word. Beautiful, when I've never considered a man to be beautiful before in my life.

What in the hell is he doing talking to me?

"Because any man who is texting you instead of being here by your side isn't worth your time."

"And let me guess, you are?"

He takes a sip from his drink but keeps those eyes on mine over the rim of his glass. "That remains to be seen now, doesn't it?"

I snort and give a roll of my eyes. "No offense, but I think you're barking up the wrong tree." I may say the words but hell if I can't stop staring at the man. I'm not sure if it's the dim lights of the club or just him in general, but he gives off a vibe that makes me want to step closer and see if it's real.

"Why's that?"

"What'll you have?" the bartender interrupts.

"Tom Collins, please," I say and slide a ten-dollar bill across the bar top.

"Another Johnnie Walker Blue," the man beside me says as he holds up his glass.

"Thank you, but I don't need you to buy my drink."

"I'm aware you don't," he says, pulling my money back and putting it in front of me as he replaces it with a twenty. "But oblige me."

Oblige him? Like that's a term you hear someone use every day.

"Thank you," I murmur.

"So, *Tom Collins.*" There's that grin of his. "Why is it that I'm barking up the wrong tree?"

"Well, *Johnnie Walker,* I assure you that whoever you're looking for, I'm not her."

His eyes take a long, languorous appraisal of my body, my skin heating under the intensity of his gaze before he gives the slightest nod. "That's where we disagree, then."

I give a half laugh and shake my head. "Glad you think so, but I'm sure you have women falling at your feet most days and—"

"True. I mean it's a tough gig, but somebody has to do it, right?" He gives a half-cocked smirk that is so stunning it's breathtaking.

For fuck's sake, why is his arrogance so sexy? Why does his stoic expression and those words falling from his lips do things to my insides? But it's the chuckle that he emits, the one that rumbles its way between the apex of my thighs, that has me giving a little shake of my shoulders.

"Cute, but rest assured, I don't beg, and I'm far from interested."

Who the hell is this girl right now?

"Is that a challenge?" he asks, those eyes of his freezing me in my place as a ghost of a smirk plays on his lips.

"It's a fact."

"Everyone begs. When it's good enough . . . *you beg.*"

"Smooth. I bet you get all the girls with lines like that."

Another chuckle. A deliberate sip of his whiskey that says I just might be right. A glance away and then back at me.

"Shh." He leans in closer and lowers his voice. "I'm not one to kiss and tell."

"Why me?" I ask.

"Why you, what?"

"Why are you buying me a drink instead of one of these other ladies?" I look at the various women lining the bar.

"Does it matter?"

"It matters."

"Because of Betty Bradshaw."

"Betty who?" I laugh.

"Betty Bradshaw. She broke my heart in the third grade when she dumped me after I bought her Twinkies instead of Ding Dongs."

"A girl after my own heart," I tease. "Everyone knows a Ding Dong is better."

The look of disdain mixed with the grin he's fighting from the ridiculousness of my words has my own smile widening.

Yes. I did just actually say Ding Dongs are better to a sexy man.

Johnnie clears his throat. "For the record, Betty broke my heart. Right there in the middle of the attendance line. She told me she preferred Jimmy Rodgers because he brought her Ding Dongs and not Twinkies."

"And what, pray tell, does this have anything to do with why you offered to buy me a drink?"

"Absolutely nothing." He flashes a boyish smile. "But I thought it might keep you here a little longer so it was worth a shot."

"Ah, clever *and* handsome."

"It's a hard combination to beat." He taps his glass against mine. "You should try it."

All I can do is shake my head and smile into my drink. Is this flirting? Is he actually flirting with me?

It feels weird and exciting and yet, I just broke up with Clint hours ago. I should not be flirting. I should be . . .

"I'll ask it again, Collins," he murmurs just above the fray. "Why am I barking up the wrong tree?"

I study this man who makes me feel uncomfortable in all the best kinds of ways. I know the last thing I need right now is to stand here and flirt with him, and the best way to prevent it is to be dead honest. A player like him will run at the first sight of what's perceived to be an emotionally unstable woman.

"Because I just broke up with my boyfriend. Anything with me would be a rebound and we know how those go."

He doesn't flinch. "Messy. Complicated. Fleeting." He smirks and gives a shrug as if he'd be up for the task. "Rebounds can be a good thing."

Well, that just backfired.

And why am I glad that it did?

"Or they can be a disaster," I counter.

"Not if you pick the right person to rebound with."

"Let me guess, you like to play the part because of the *fleeting* portion of your answer? Less strings. No attachment."

"That and the great sex."

"Should I assume that you provide them with the *great* part of that sentence?"

"We'll just say I'm a definite, contributing factor," he says with zero shame.

"You sure think highly of yourself."

"It's not my fault women aren't looked after properly. I mean, if a man can't find his way around a woman's body . . . is he even a man?"

I snort and roll my eyes.

"Are you telling me I'm wrong? Are you telling me that your ex cared about your needs as much as you did his? Was sex a duty and not something you looked forward to?"

Yes. I scream the word in my head as I think of Clint and how boring sex had gotten. Lay down. Spread legs. Moan and fake it. He groans and rolls over. And then how I'd consider if it was worth bothering to finish myself off after his breathing evened out and his soft snores filled the room. Mostly? It wasn't.

Then again, maybe it had always been boring. Maybe I had loved him so much at the beginning that I overlooked the lackluster sex. And then as time progressed and animosity set in, I just participated rather than enjoyed it.

"Huh." It's the only thing he says but rest assured it sounds like, *you know I'm right.*

"How long were you with him?"

"Two years."

"Two years with the same person? *Christ.*"

"Monogamy not your thing?"

"Didn't say that." He gives a half-hearted shrug and shifts on his feet.

"You didn't have to. You implied it."

"You make a lot of assumptions," he murmurs. He places a finger on the condensation about to slide from my glass then lifts it to his mouth and licks it off.

My attention is drawn to his tongue. Hell, any woman with a pulse would be.

"Just as I'm sure you've made them about me."

"And what assumptions do you think I've made about you?" He's bumped from behind and takes a step closer to me. He smells of fresh air and the outdoors. It's a subtle scent but one that owns my attention nonetheless.

Much like he does.

"Hmm. That I'm easy. That I'm so desperate for attention that I'm

23

here in a bar looking for it any way I can find it." I purse my lips and stare at him as I try to figure out what else to say. "That you sure as hell hope I like Starbucks so you can take me there in the morning."

"*Starbucks?*" He coughs out a perplexed laugh. "You just lost me, Collins."

"In case you forget my name since I'd probably become one among many of your one-night conquests, so the name part might get a bit foggy. It lets you save face. It's better for you if the barista asks my name to put on my order than if you do."

Johnnie stares at me with a dumbfounded expression. But his smile mesmerizes me and the amusement in his eyes has me wanting more of his attention.

"That's actually quite brilliant."

"Thank you."

"So *do you?*" he asks.

"Do I what?"

"Like Starbucks?"

There's something about him that makes me feel daring. Comfortable. A little not like myself. I lean in close to him and whisper in his ear. "I'm an Americano with two sugars kind of girl, but I doubt you'd forget the name *Collins.*"

Quit while you're ahead, Sutton. You might be pulling off the mysterious and flirty thing but it won't last. You're seconds away from devolving into the awkward, fumbling idiot, so take the win and walk away while you can.

And with that exact thought, I take my first step, trip over something—probably my own feet in the universe's way of letting me know I'm not all that cool—and fall toward him. My hand lands on his crotch seconds before my face almost collides with his shoulder.

But I catch myself. Somehow, I gain leverage by pushing against his crotch and shoving myself backwards. He emits a grunt followed by a grimace, and as I steady myself, marveling at how I didn't spill my drink while registering the exact size of what I felt beneath his pants.

My cheeks flush, and it's way easier for me to take a long sip of my drink than meet his eyes.

"Jesus." He chuckles. "If you wanted to test the goods, all you had to do was ask."

This time he earns the roll of my eyes. It's the only thing I can think to do other than die of embarrassment. "You really need to work on getting better pickup lines."

"And you need to work on making better assumptions."

Our eyes meet, hold, assess. "Are you telling me I'm wrong?" I ask, suddenly on the defensive. "That you're not here on the prowl? Looking for a good time with a willing woman? Thinking you've found an easy target with me?"

"An easy target? You? Hardly." He gives a quick shake of his head but his eyes tell me there is interest there.

Interest I both want and don't know how to feel about.

This is all new to me. Foreign. Being hit on in a club. *Wanting* to be hit on in a club.

Desire in general.

What the hell do I do next?

Live a little. Enjoy feeling attractive and wanted.

Nerves rattle around inside of me as my bravado wanes.

"And for the record, I'm in town for work. Figured I'd grab a few drinks and relax before having to deal with my partners tomorrow."

"I take it you don't like them?"

He purses his lips for a beat before answering. "It's complicated."

"Isn't everything?" I shift on my feet. "Thank you for the drink. It was nice meeting you, Johnnie. Good luck with your partners tomorrow and more importantly, in your quest to find your morning Starbucks date."

"Where's the fun in that, Collins?" He takes a step closer.

"I know rejection isn't something you're used to, but yes, I came here to celebrate my newly single status and my huge promotion at work with my friend. And now I'm going to return to that celebration."

"A promotion? Nice. Congrats." He taps his glass to mine.

"Yes. Thank you. They're over there." I motion to the velvet-roped area where Lizzy is sitting in the center of a group of guys. He looks to them and then back to me.

"Go celebrate then."

"I will."

"Off you go."

"I'm going."

"Then why aren't your feet moving?"

Because I don't want them to.

I should want them to. I should want the hell away from all men. I should be traumatized after what I allowed Clint to do to me . . . but it feels so good to flirt. So good to see a man look at me with desire. So incredible to be turned on . . . that my feet don't want to move.

"*Well?*"

Panic strikes.

Sheer and utter panic.

"*Who would have you if you left me, Sutton? No one else will find you attractive.*"

"I will," I say. "Right now."

Keeping my nerves in check, I walk past him and toward the first exit, every step urgently hoping my brain will stop replaying Clint's vicious words. Shoving the door open, I welcome the sudden silence, the cool air on my face, and the immediate distance between me and a man who flusters me in ways I've never experienced.

It's been two years since you've flirted, Sutt. It's okay to be unnerved and unsettled and not sure how to feel.

Deep breath.

Slow, deep breaths.

I look around the dimly lit alley where people come and go a few feet from me and welcome the moment's peace to gather my bearings and not feel like more of an idiot for running from *Johnnie Walker.*

"What are you doing?" I mutter to myself. *What woman walks away from a man like that?* Why can't I allow myself to enjoy something a little forbidden and let loose after two years of whatever it was?

Go back in there, Sutton.

You deserve to feel good after getting the promotion today.

Go back and see where the night takes you.

You deserve to feel something exciting after feeling so numb for so long.

Do one more *thing for yourself.*

I laugh at myself, my new motto (apparently), and draw in a deep breath to fortify my courage before I do something completely out of the ordinary and wildly inappropriate. *The problem?* When I go to open the door, it's locked. Clearly, they don't want random people walking in from outside who haven't paid the cover charge.

I'm a few steps down the alley toward the front entrance of Club Coquette when the door is shoved open behind me. "Collins." I turn to see *him* standing there, framed in the light of the door closing at his back while goosebumps chase over my skin. "Don't go."

My bravado returns as he closes the distance and stops right in front of me. "I thought you didn't beg," I say.

He emits the sexiest groan before he pushes me against the wall at my back and takes the kiss he's been working for all night.

And holy hell can this man kiss.

CHAPTER FOUR

Sutton

Nine Hours Ago

M Y BODY BURNS—EVERY MUSCLE, EVERY NERVE ENDING, every inch of my skin—as our mouths brand and tongues taste and teeth nip. If I thought our kisses in the club's alley and then in the backseat of our taxi to his impressive suite at The Mark were incredible, I was severely underestimating the talent of this man.

And I'm definitely not complaining.

But now as his hands slide down to cup my ass while we stumble our way into his suite, all I can think about is how I want more. Him naked. Him filling me. *Him fucking me.*

Desire this intense is completely new to me, and I plan to revel in every damn second of it.

Alcohol and the lack of inhibition it brings me is more than welcome as we discard our clothes in a flurry of movements. My dress. His shirt. My bra. His pants. Each one kicked or thrown aside without thought as our lips continue to find one another's and our hands begin to explore.

My hands immediately go to his strong shoulders, run down abs I can't see in the dim light but can feel ridge after ridge of. Impatient, I slip my hand beneath the waistband of his boxer briefs where his more than impressive bulge is all but testing the integrity of its fabric. He's warm and hard and thick and the feel of him only makes the ache to have him even sweeter.

He dips down and out of reach so that his mouth can languish on my breast. My hands, desperate to have a purpose, thread through his hair. His tongue circles my nipple before his lips close over it and he sucks. The soft moan that is low in my throat becomes strangled as his hand finds its way beneath the waistband of my panties. His fingers part me, sliding between the slick flesh he finds there, and his groan melds with my quick intake of air.

"All this for me?" he murmurs against my skin as he laces open-mouthed kisses back up to the curve of my neck. I don't speak, can't, because my focus is on the feel of his hair between my fingers, the warmth of his breath on my neck, and the utter bliss as he lifts my foot onto a nearby chair before tucking a finger into me.

My breath catches and my knees become pliant as he slides that finger back out and up to my clit. He gently rubs over the bundle of nerves there so that I'm practically pushing my pussy into his hand to do more, to make me feel more. With each addition of friction, sensations ignite fireworks within my core.

His mouth finds mine again. "You didn't answer me, Collins," he murmurs between kisses. "I asked you if this is all for me."

My brain is trying to fire but it's so focused on his fingers. How they slide back between my seam. How they push into me and hit exactly where they need to hit inside me.

I'm shocked into the now when Johnnie fists his hand in my hair and pulls my head back. My mouth falls open and my neck is exposed as I'm forced to look into those amber eyes that are inches from mine.

"Your ex may have allowed you to be silent, but that's because he was a selfish prick. I want to hear you say what you want. I want to know I'm making you feel how you want to feel. I want the neighbors on either side of these walls to call the front desk because you're screaming so loud one minute and begging me for more the next. Is that understood?" The dark promise of his words feels like a rumble through my body. A finger flipping a light switch on. A tremor of adrenaline-laced desire.

His hold on my hair prevents me from looking away like I normally would. There is no room to be shy. No space to back away and collect myself. There is only the ragged rasp of my breath and the slick sound of my arousal as his fingers continue to work their way so casually in and out of me. *It's as if he owns me.*

I have never been more turned on in my life.

"The woman in Coquette had no problem firing a quick comeback and telling me what she thought of me. Was that confidence all a show?" He twists his fingers tighter in my hair, adding the tiniest bit of pain. His eyebrow raises, a silent challenge to see if I'm as mouthy here as I was in the bar. "Now tell me, Collins, what is it that you want?"

My breath shudders as my body edges closer to that high, his words only spurring my arousal on.

I've never been spoken to like this. I've never been asked, demanded, coaxed—whatever you want to call it—to express what I want in bed. It had always been Clint's needs that came first. It had always been me feeling so dissatisfied. Frustrated. *Wanting.*

And it's both heady and empowering to be spoken to this way. To be asked to voice what I want.

I'll never see this man again. Hell, we don't even know each other's names . . . so isn't this my chance to just go for it? To wear the shoes of whoever this woman I'm being tonight and enjoy the ride?

Pun intended.

So I take a slow, fortifying breath, my eyes meeting his stare for stare, and say something I've never uttered in my entire life. "I want you to fuck me. I want you to make me feel. I want you to make me come."

His fingers still inside me as his approving chuckle rumbles through the room. "There she is," he croons as a smile curves his lips. "I love a woman who knows what she wants." He presses a teasing kiss to my lips and then whispers, "But you have to earn my cock first, Collins."

His words surprise me and even though he releases my hair and pulls his fingers out from inside me, I stand there slack-jawed and unsatisfied. "I have to *what?*"

He makes this the perfect time to slide down his boxer briefs so that his cock springs free. And of course, someone as gorgeous as him would have to have a perfect dick. Thick and hard and *Jesus* . . . he was right. *Some things are worth begging for.*

And *that* is one of them.

"You heard me," he says, pulling my attention back to him as he takes a step toward me. "You have to earn it."

"I—"

"Take off your panties, Collins." His eyes lower as I slide my soaked panties down my hips and step out of them when they hit my ankles. Nerves flutter about as he takes a long, slow appraisal of my body. That cocky tilt to his lips is back when his eyes meet mine again. "Stand in front of the window, Collins."

"But—"

"Do as I say," he commands softly as if to let me know that refusing isn't an option. "It's time to work for that fuck you want." He quirks a brow. "Now over to the window."

I obey.

God, I never thought I'd say those words in my entire life, but I *fucking obey.*

And I do so with more eagerness than I've showed for something in a long time.

There is no room for modesty as I do what he asks. No room when he looks at me with an intensity that is strong enough to light me on fire, let alone the room.

"Good girl," he purrs and runs a hand down my jaw before twirling his finger in the air. "Now turn around and put your hands on the glass. Yes, just like that." A soft hand over the curve of my ass. "You like that, don't you, Collins? To be seen. To know anyone can look up here at any second and see you standing here. To know that someone right now might be getting off while watching you stand there naked." He runs a finger softly between my thighs. His touch so featherlight that it takes everything I have not to push my ass back to feel more. "Tell me, Collins. Tell me you like it."

"I like it." Breathless. Desperate.

"Better," he praises, his mouth at my ear. "Now bend over, press your tits against the glass, and let me see that gorgeous pussy of yours."

I do as he asks, bending over and sticking my ass out.

The room is silent as I stand there. I can only assume he is behind me, staring, and the inability to see him and what he's doing, heightens the anticipation that has been building, sensation by sensation.

His lips touch the small of my back, and I jolt at the unexpected sensation. "You have such a beautiful pussy, Collins. It's"—he emits a guttural groan when his fingertip rubs ever so gently over my wet folds—"such a turn-on."

I try to push back onto his hand, clenching my muscles when I do. His chuckle is seductive as it rumbles through the room. "Are you asking for something? Is your pussy tightening for me?"

God.

Yes.

Please.

"Mm-hmm," is all I can manage.

"Answer me or I stop." His touch leaves me and my body tenses in response.

"Yes. That's for you."

Take it. Please fucking take it, because I'm aching and soaked and all I can think about is your next touch.

But the silence returns. The expectation builds.

His hand slides over one side of my ass, between my thighs just enough to tease my opening before running over the other cheek. I feel the heat of his body behind me. Can smell the scent of his cologne mixed with my arousal. "I should take you like this right here, against the glass for everyone to see." His fingers press a little closer this trip around. "But I want to watch you. Your tits. Your lips. Your sweet pussy. *You.* Is that what you want, Collins?"

"Yes," I moan, his fingers back where I want them again. A hiss of pleasure falls from my lips when the wet, warmth of his mouth closes over me. The ache . . . oh my God, the ache the simplest touch of his tongue creates is enough to have me pushing myself back against him. Wanting him to take more. Needing him to take more.

He closes his mouth over my most intimate skin, taking it in his mouth and sucking. It's a sensation I've never experienced before and sure as hell want to experience again. Pressure builds within me. The burn of desire shifts into bliss I've never experienced before.

"You like that? My mouth on you? My tongue in you?" He licks up the line of my spine. Chills chase his tongue every inch of the way, until the heat of his breath is on my neck. "Your pussy is beautiful, Collins.

The way it looks. The way it tastes. The way it tightens at my touch." He pulls my hair back exposing my neck. "It's time to get on the bed. I want you on your back. Thighs spread. Eyes on me. Yes?"

It's amazing what desperation will do. To want something so damn strong you'll do things you swore you'd never do. Like obeying a man you just met.

But I do it.

I move to the bed, lie down, and spread my thighs.

A thousand lights of the city are at his back, but my eyes are on him. They couldn't be anywhere else right now. He owns my attention.

He takes a few steps toward me, his tongue darting out to wet his lips—lips still coated with my arousal—as he steps out of the shadows. And even though I'm watching him, I jolt when he runs a fingertip up the inside of my calf. It's not because I'm uncertain or scared. No, I'm desperate for more.

Of his lips on me.

Of his hands touching me.

Of the way he looks at me.

His hand strokes back and forth over his cock. He even makes that look sexy as he wipes a thumb over his precum and rubs it over his crest. Every part of my body tenses in anticipation as he unknowingly teases me.

"Christ, you're stunning," he murmurs. "I'm going to need to taste more of that."

And just as my brain registers his words, he kneels between my spread legs—his hands on my thighs—and dips his head. *Oh God. So good.*

The guttural groan he emits is everything. Its vibration only adds to the onslaught of sensations his mouth, and now his fingers are adding to the mix as they slip back into me.

I'm already primed. Already turned on. Already swimming in a sea of sensations familiar and yet so very unfamiliar to me. Going down on me wasn't a priority for Clint. And when he did, he was lazy and fumbling.

Johnnie, on the other hand . . . is skilled at it. Every damn aspect of it. The way he touches. The way he licks. Everything.

I feel in sensations. The scrape of his stubble against the inside of my thighs. The warmth of his mouth. The pressure of his hands as he spreads my thighs as far apart as they'll go. The shock as his tongue pushes its way into me.

A strangled moan falls from the back of my throat as my body coils tighter and tighter. I reach for anything and everything. The sheets. His hair. My heels dig in against his shoulders as my legs tense and my body climbs.

His pace quickens. Fingers and tongue and movement and pressure. The rhythm is relentless. One I can't escape from even if I wanted to.

"*Right there.*"

My head falls back.

"*Just like that.*"

My back arches.

"*Please.*"

My hips buck into his face.

"*Oh. My. God.*"

All shame is gone as the coil snaps. My body shudders. My voice grates over the word *Yes* as I'm thrown headfirst into wave after wave of ecstasy.

I'm breathless and flushed and overwhelmed as he crawls over me and smothers my mewls with his lips. I taste myself on his tongue, and I swear to God, it sends another round of pulses through my pussy.

"Christ, woman." He gently tugs on my bottom lip and my eyes flash open. I offer a sleep-drugged smile as I come down from my high.

"The tongue definitely works." I laugh, feeling emboldened, and make a check-mark sign with my finger.

"I'm being graded, huh?" he asks as he scrapes his teeth over my collarbone and heads toward my breasts. "Then I guess I better get back to work. There are more places I plan on exploring."

He cups one of my breasts, his thumb flicking over my pebbled nipple while his mouth closes around the other one. I squirm beneath his touch, my body still hypersensitive from my orgasm. My squirming only serves to grind my thigh against the thickness of his cock.

"Greedy, are we?" he asks, lips moving against my skin.

"Yes. Do you have a problem with greedy girls?" I smile at him as I shift so that I can wrap my hand around his dick. He sucks in a quick breath and runs the stubble of his chin down the rest of my abdomen before sitting up on his haunches and staring at me.

The man is gorgeous. Simply put. From his eyes to his hair to his body to his cock. He's a damn Adonis, and all I can fathom as I lie here with a goofy grin on my face in my post orgasmic haze is that it's a travesty I almost denied myself this.

"No problem at all." He angles his head to the side. "Just trying to figure out what to do with you next."

"You could put that to good use," I say and try to reach for his cock again. "Or . . ." I trail a finger over his thigh, wanting to touch his veined shaft again and getting heady off my newfound confidence. "Turn-about could be fair play."

He lifts a lone eyebrow as his mouth turns up at one corner. "It could, could it?" he murmurs as I sit up to match his posture.

"It definitely could." And this time, when I go to wrap my hand around his cock, he lets me. My fingers don't make the circle but by the way his eyes fall half closed and the moan he emits, I don't really think he minds.

I lean forward and swirl my tongue over its tip, welcoming the taste of his precum with a murmur of appreciation.

His hand fists in my hair, pulling my head back. "If you're going to suck my cock, Collins, I want to see all of you while you do it." He shifts out of my grasp and moves to stand at the edge of the bed. "Come here." He moves me so that I'm lying on my back with my neck angled over the edge of the bed. I'm looking at him upside down from my position on the bed.

"I don't underst—"

"I'm big." He gives a shameless but arrogant shrug. "This will help open the back of your throat up so you can take more of me in."

Well, *holy hell*. I think I just came again from those words alone.

He leans over and gives me a backwards kiss, our faces in opposing positions before he straightens up so that my lips are met with every long inch of him.

I open my mouth and take him in. A slide of my tongue around his bell-shaped crest. A sheathing of my teeth as he stretches my lips. A suction of my lips around his girth as I lift my hand to give the base of his shaft some love because there is no way in hell I'll be able to fit his entirety in my mouth.

"Fuck," he groans. He slowly begins to move his hips so that his cock slides in and out of my mouth while I suction around him. "That feels incredible."

He is measured in his movements. His restraint noticeable in the tensing of his thigh where my other hand rests. But he slowly works his cock in and out of my mouth, each slide in a little bit farther than the one before.

He's definitely big and it takes me a few times to measure my breathing and gag reflex to not choke when he hits the back of my throat. But the groans he makes, the ones that rumble around the room as I suck tightly around him, only serve to make me want more of him.

"I can see when I hit your throat, Collins. How your muscles tighten around me when I go deeper." He runs a fingertip over the side of my cheek and to my neck when he pushes into the depths of my mouth. "Your nipples are hard." He palms one of them and flicks a thumb over my nipple. "I love the way you push your pussy in the air each time I fuck your mouth, almost as if you're pretending my cock is fucking you there too." He slides his finger between the seam of my sex but does nothing more. I buck my hips up as his touch leaves me. "Do you want it that bad? Do you want this"—he grinds his hips in a circle so his dick hits the inside of my cheek—"fucking you into oblivion? Do you want to know what satisfaction feels like?"

"Please," I try to say around his cock as I move my hand from his thigh to snake it down between my thighs, the ache growing so intense I need to help ease it.

"What was that?" he asks.

"Please," I repeat and then moan as my fingers find my clit.

"See?" he says with a pained chuckle as he leans back, a gasp falling from my lips as his cock slips out and his tongue replaces it in my mouth. The kiss is hungry and fueled with a violent desire that until now, I don't think I ever could have understood.

But I do now.

Oh, God, how I do now.

"Good things are worth begging for."

"Yes." I nip his lip. "God, yes." My tongue delves into his mouth as my hands grip the back of his neck. "Fuck me, now."

And before my sex-drugged synapses can fire, Johnnie has hauled me up by my shoulders and has me bent over the bed. His hands knead my breasts as his body flanks mine from behind. The heat of his labored breath is against my ear. The feel of his wet cock presses between my thighs. The scrape of his stubble teases my skin as he runs his chin back and forth over my shoulder.

"How do you want to come this time, Collins?" He scrapes his teeth over the curve of my neck. "From behind? Against the wall in the shower? With you riding me?" His hands slide down my sides, and he angles one so that his fingers can rub ever so softly over my clit. "Maybe we'll try all three. One for each orgasm."

"I can't—"

"Oh, you definitely can."

A gasp of my breath. A spread farther apart of my legs. "But I've never . . ." *been able to come more than once.*

I don't utter the words because my breath hitches as his other hand slides down the crease of my ass. No one has ever touched me there and my body tenses as his other finger presses gently on the rim of muscles.

He's got me. If I writhe away from the pressure on my clit, I push into his other hand on my ass. If I go the opposite, my body gets the pleasure but not the release.

"You will come at least two more times, Collins. Maybe even more." The steadfast assurance in his voice, the confidence, is enough to cause that ache to intensify. Enough for me to believe his promise.

"I can't—" I moan with a shake of my head, not sure if I want him to stop or never stop as the intensity of his touch grows.

He fists my hair and pulls sharply so that my head is back and my neck is exposed. "Are you saying you doubt my abilities? That you don't think I can make you come until you feel broken?"

He licks a line up the length of my neck and I swear to everything holy, my body aches for him to never stop touching me. It burns in places I never knew could burn. My nipples. My mouth. My pussy. *My skin.*

I've been touched before. I've had sex before. But nothing like this. *Nothing ever like this.*

To feel powerful and powerless at the same time is a heady feeling that makes me want to bask in its newness.

To have a man so confident in his touch and arrogant in his demands is a turn-on I never knew I needed. *Or wanted.*

To have a man in control but who's not controlling. One whose demands are only to bring me pleasure. To only make me want more.

His fingers bring me right to that edge—where my hands fist and my body starts to tense and breath starts to labor—and then he backs off.

"Tell me what you want," he demands.

"You," I pant, needing his fingers, his cock, his *anything* in me to help me come. "I want you."

My words are like the flick of a light switch because he emits the sexiest growl I've ever heard as he flips me over on my back so that my ass is on the edge of the bed. He stands between my thighs, his eyes running over the length of my body as he slides the condom on.

But then his eyes find mine again at the same time that he rubs the crest of his cock up and down against my center. We both suck in an audible breath at the initial sensation—this moment having been built up over the past hour.

"You think you can take all of me?" He quirks a brow as he throws down a challenge I am more than up for.

"There's only one way to find out." My last word becomes a moan as he pushes his way oh-so-slowly into me.

My eyes roll back and my lips fall open as the pleasurable burn of my body stretching to accept him amplifies. He pushes as far in as he can until he bottoms out and then just sits there so I can adjust.

"You good?" he murmurs, eyes half closed with pleasure, and tendons taut in his neck as he tries to hold on to his control.

"Yes. Oh my God, yes."

It's all I can manage to say as we both look down to watch him pull out for the first time. My arousal glistens on his cock. That's the hottest thing ever, to see my skin stretching around him as he withdraws.

"You feel amazing," he murmurs as his hands find my hips and he helps lift them up as he thrusts back into me.

I'm on sensation overload. The way his head hits the patch of nerves. The rub of his thumb over my clit when he pulls back out. The way he fills me like I've never been filled before.

Each one is a new experience. Each one something I focus on and drown in simultaneously.

"Please," I beg as I buck my hips up, needing more friction, *more of him*, to reach that climax he's been edging me toward for some time.

He leans over and grabs the back of my neck, pulling me toward him so that his lips can find mine. The movement pushes him even deeper within me and our moan-fueled kiss as he moves in and out of me is erotic in every sense of the word.

"I need more," I say between kisses. "More."

His chuckle is barely audible over the slick sounds of him fucking me. "You sure you're ready?"

I grip his biceps. "Now. Fuck me, now."

And thank God, he obliges me because he picks up the pace. A little harder on the thrust in. A lot more urgent on the piston out. I try to meet him with each movement, but thoughts escape me in much the same way as having control over my body right now.

All I can focus on is him.

And the slapping sound when our centers meet.

And the way he makes my nerves burn so bright I'd swear they were made of fire.

His fingers dig into the flesh of my hips.

My pulse roars in my ears and all I can focus on is that spot. The one he keeps rubbing with each movement. Over and over and over.

The orgasm slams into me like a freight train. There's no other way to describe the utter devastation it has on me or the current of bliss that ricochets through my body with each and every wave. My toes curl, my legs tense, and my pussy pulses around him. My eyes close and I emit the most guttural groan I've ever heard.

"Fuck," he groans as he keeps going, keeps fucking, until it's his voice crying out as he chases his own.

He collapses onto the bed beside me as we both gasp for breath and try to process the incredulity that just was.

"Fuck, Collins," Johnnie murmurs. He leans up on an elbow and captures my mouth with his again. "You are incredible and I'm going to need to have you again."

CHAPTER FIVE

Sutton

Four Hours Ago

"I NEED ONE MORE TASTE OF YOU BEFORE I GO."

I half chuckle, half sigh as I feel the silkiness of Johnnie's hair against my inner thighs and the warmth of his tongue licking its way between my now swollen slit.

My legs are slightly sore but the tightness is quickly forgotten as the mastery of his tongue makes everything else fade away.

Does the man ever tire?

Considering my orgasm slowly simmering beneath the surface, for my sake, I'm glad he doesn't.

I close my eyes and sink into the pleasure he provides—

Ring.

I bolt up in bed, slightly disoriented in the dim light of the unfamiliar room and try to catch my startled breath.

The phone.

Get the phone.

I look at the nightstand beside me where the phone is lit up as it rings and scramble over to grab it.

"Hello?" I say in my sleep garbled voice.

"Good morning, ma'am," a very efficient-sounding woman says. "I just wanted to let you know that your order is on the way up. The concierge will leave it at the door for you."

"I didn't order anything . . ." I take a quick look around the hotel room and realize there is absolutely zero trace of the man I was with last night. My purse and phone are still on the table across the way.

"Someone did and he had very exact instructions on delivery time and process," she says. "Please let us know if you need anything else."

"Thank you."

I slide out of bed and pull the comforter around me as I walk toward the bathroom. A part of me deflates when there isn't a trace of him in there, nor is he in the sitting room of the suite.

He's gone.

I walk around the room. The wrappers from the minibar we raided at three in the morning aren't strewn across the table. My clothes are folded neatly on the couch. I move about and then breathe a sigh of relief to see the trash can full of empty water bottles and trash.

Last night did happen. I don't need to be pinched to confirm it wasn't a dream. The evidence is all right there.

And I'm not sure why I so desperately needed to see it to believe it.

A little more settled, I notice my handprints on the glass windows. They're a visual reminder of last night, with the early morning sky just beginning to light up outside, and I feel a mixture of validation, sadness, relief, and something else that I can't quite put my finger on.

Sadness because it's over.

Sure, I knew it was a one-night stand going in, but I can't deny that I enjoyed every damn minute of it. Him. What he brought out in me. The things he showed me were possible during sex. The things he made me realize I had done without and now never would settle for again.

Relief because it's over.

Him not being here means there is no morning-after awkwardness, no demonstration of the weird and sudden clinginess I feel toward him, no need to make excuses and explain how so very out of the ordinary it was for me to do that last night.

That it's not my MO.

And then there is the something *else.*

The emptiness? The acknowledgment that I don't know how to do a one-night stand and so . . . I feel a little lost.

There has to be some validity in that, right?

Or maybe it's just coming to terms with everything that has happened in the last twenty or so hours. Maybe I look at last night and Johnnie Walker and think of it *and him* as a well-needed jolt to my system. As proof or validation or something to show me that I was right to find the courage to finally leave Clint. *And I feel so damn free.*

All I know is his scent is still on my skin and every time I notice it, I'm reminded of how little sleep we got and how many orgasms I achieved.

Of the laughter and the moans and the groans that filled this room.

Of how I let myself be someone else for a few hours and don't regret it one bit.

Oh. My. God.

Last night really happened.

It did.

And practical, dependable, colors-insides-the-lines Sutton Pierce literally just had her brains fucked out by a man—perfection in the male form—without a single regret.

I squeal and cover my face with my hands like a silly teenager.

The knock on the door startles me even though I should have expected it.

I wait until I hear the footsteps fade down the hall and the elevator ding before I open the door to the suite. When I look down, there is the unmistakable Starbucks logo on a brown bag and a cup of coffee beside it.

I pick up the coffee and belt out a laugh. "Collins" is printed in black Sharpie on the side of it.

He didn't forget.

With a goofy smile on my face, I grab the bag of bakery goods and head toward the table, because I'm famished. It's only when I go to open the bag that I notice the handwritten note on the outside of it.

Thanks for last night. Hope the rebound was worth it.
—Johnnie

CHAPTER SIX

Sutton

T HERE ARE THINGS YOU SAY DURING A ONE-NIGHT STAND. Admissions you make. Liberties you take. Inhibitions you forget. And all of those are done with the presumption that you never plan on seeing that person again.

Ever.

You let yourself be someone else for a while, only ever expecting to revisit it in your own mind. Thinking the memory of the man is probably way better than the reality of him.

At least that's what a logical, practical, newly single person like me would assume.

Yet ... here I sit in a conference room across from three gorgeous men whose company acronym is aptly named S.I.N. And one of those men is currently living rent free in my head while at the same time, is the culprit of the slight soreness I feel when I shift in my chair.

How is this even happening?

"You think you can take all of it?"

"I'm sorry?" I startle and note three sets of amber eyes staring at me. I all but choke upon hearing *those words*. I'm immediately taken back to Johnnie standing between my parted thighs, stroking himself as he asked that same question. "You caught me mid-note," I try to explain by holding my pen up as if that will make them understand. "What did you ask again?"

"I asked if you think you can handle it?" Ledger leans back in his chair and angles his head as he stares at me. There is curiosity in his eyes and God knows if I were in his shoes, I'd be more than worried about the woman tasked with taking on my project. Considering every time I meet one of their eyes, I'm reliving the events of last night. "Roz has assured us that you are well versed in what it takes to assess the problems and address the issues as they come with a resort of this size. As I'm sure you know, S.I.N. has a reputation for impeccable service and stately accommodations. Having a resort underperform, as this one has, is a blemish on our portfolio and we don't particularly like blemishes. We need to turn this around and turn it around promptly."

"Understood." *Fake it till you make it.* "I've been over the financials, the anonymous employee surveys, the guest reviews, as well as dug around a little to see what the competition offers that you don't. Rest assured there is hope. The main thing we need is to get the staff on board with strong leadership, and once they realize the ship isn't sinking, that we're there and present, your staff confidence will improve too."

"Agreed. Callahan will be your point person," Ford says, pointing to his brother. From the look they exchange, there's some kind of tension there. But when Callahan looks my way and gives me a curt nod, all signs of it are erased.

"Apparently I'm the only one available for the job," he says lifting a hand, and for a split second, I'm dead certain he is Johnnie Walker. There's something in his eyes—amusement laced with mischief—that makes me feel like we're part of an inside joke.

But then of course, when Ledger speaks, our connection is broken, and I question my own judgment.

How could I not?

"Great. I'll make sure I provide twice-daily updates, if that works for you. We can have set times to talk if that—"

"There's no need." Ledger smiles. "He'll be on-site with you."

"On-site?" I muster a smile. *Lovely.* So not only will I be working with the company of Johnnie Walker, I might possibly be working side by side with him. This turn of events is so ridiculous, it's comical. "Perfect."

"Yes. Normally we manage from afar and let the resort manager handle things, but like we said, this project needs to be turned around quickly. We figure having both you and Cal on location will be beneficial in making this happen," Ford explains.

Callahan glances briefly at his brother.

Definitely tension there.

"Despite the warning signs, he was the one so gung-ho on us buying this resort in the first place," Ledger interjects, "so it's only fair that he gets the satisfaction of turning it around." He glances at both of his brothers, giving them a look that almost feels like a warning, before turning back to smile warmly at Roz and me. "From the praises Roz sings about you, Sutton, I'm sure the two of you will work well together."

I stare at the three of them with what I can assume is another *deer in the headlights* look on my face as I try to *not* relive any of last night while under their scrutiny.

"I'm sure we'll get along just fine," Callahan says.

"I'm sure we will," I repeat, suddenly desperate to get out of here.

"See, gentlemen?" Roz interrupts with a smug smile. "I told you Sutton was the right person for the job."

"It seems she is," one of the men murmurs in a way that has goosebumps forming, but when I look from Roz to the three of them sitting across from us, I'm not certain which one it was.

But I swear to God, it was *Johnnie* speaking.

CHAPTER SEVEN

Callahan

THE DOOR SHUTS.

Their heels clicking on the marble tile just beyond the door an audible reminder that yes, that did in fact just happen.

Collins—*er, Sutton*—the woman with the sweet pussy and incredible ass that I had to drag myself away from this morning, really was just sitting across from me.

And if my eyes didn't believe what I was seeing, my raging hard-on beneath the cover of the conference room table was evidence enough.

Shock is an understatement to express exactly what I felt when she walked in here. Pure and utter fucking shock.

Her laugh echoes back toward us, and my balls draw up at the sound. Is that mark I left still on the curve of her shoulder where I bit her when I took her from behind? Do her hips have bruises from where my fingertips gripped tight?

It's normal to want her again after not having her for a few hours, right? Because the sex was that good, I'd go again right now if I could.

The fact I sent her Starbucks says enough right there.

I don't ever look back when I leave after a one-night stand. *Ever*. But I looked back. I ordered her damn coffee with her name on the cup because I wanted her to know I remembered.

And now look where that got me?

Fuck.

Suddenly, being forced to go to Ocean's Edge and abandon my regularly scheduled program isn't looking as dismal as I thought it might.

Sun, more rebound sex, and hopefully spotty cell service down in the islands, giving me an excuse not to respond to my brothers immediately, might redeem this bullshit blip of a distraction on my plans.

If my brothers are going to handcuff me, I might as well have fun in the process.

It's only then that I realize how dead silent the conference room is. I swivel in my chair to face my brothers and find both of them with their arms crossed, just sitting there watching me.

"This is a horrible fucking idea," Ford mutters under his breath.

"For once I agree with you, Ford," I finally say, turning to my brothers with a grin that will surely piss them off. *Fucking perfect.* If I'm forced to be here, to deal with their bullshit resentment, the least I can do is push some buttons while I'm at it. "Sending me to paradise with a woman who looks like *that*? Yep. Definite fucking mistake."

"Jesus Christ. Will you ever change?" Ledger says, shoving his chair back from the table so he can face me.

"Change? Change what? My attitude? My goals? My what? I wasn't aware being part owner of S.I.N. meant I couldn't appreciate a beautiful woman. Hell, I'll simply be living up to the company name."

"It means you act professional," Ford says. "It means you keep your dick in your pants and your hands off Sutton."

"Just like you did last year with what's her name?" I say, knowing I've caught him dead in the water.

"It's not the same," he counters.

"Clearly." I roll my eyes, already feeling the life being sucked out of me from sitting in this office.

"Should we remind you why we're in this situation in the first place? The name Gia ring any bells?"

Fuck you.

The two words are on the tip of my tongue but I fight them off. "Yep. You're right," I sneer. "Then again, I forgot there were Ford and Ledger rules and then there were Callahan rules. My bad." I hold my hands up and meet both of my brothers' stares dead on.

"Exactly." Ledger practically spits the word out, the animosity in the room palpable. "There's always been two sets of rules in this family." The muscle in his jaw tics as he glares at me.

"So that's what this is about?" I ask with a disbelieving snort. "Fuck me over because of something I couldn't control?"

"Speaking of fucking . . . you used the suite last night." Ledger doesn't ask. It's simply a statement to catch me off guard.

And it sure as shit does.

I think of our corporate suite. The one that we all use from time to time when clients aren't staying there. The one I used last night.

I stare at my brother, my blank expression intentional as I try to catch my bearings in this game we're playing that I'm still trying to figure out the rules to. "Keeping tabs on me too? So glad to be back under someone's thumb again."

"Nope." He shrugs. "No need to keep tabs when you do exactly what's expected of you without fail."

And there's the dig.

"And your point is what, Ledger? That I met up with someone? Do you need to see her name and credentials to make sure she's good enough for the Sharpe name?"

Fucking hell.

"You've never had any discretion in the past so why start now, right?" Ford chimes in.

"Jealousy doesn't look good on you, Ford." I fire a warning shot across the bow.

"Let's hope whoever you fucked last night was enough to satisfy you so you keep your hands off Sutton," he says, stare unwavering, warning ignored.

"What are you, my keeper now?"

"No," Ledger says. "Technically, we're your bosses."

My fist clenches and teeth grit. Power—or the perceived notion of power—sure has made my brothers absolute assholes.

No wonder I can't wait to get the fuck out of here.

"Get off it, Ledger. Last I checked, we're all equal partners, so no, you're not my boss. Furthermore, I'm a grown man who can make his own decisions about who he sleeps with."

"And we're a multi-billion-dollar corporation that doesn't exactly want to get screwed by those decisions." His smile is smarmy and patronizing, and I'd give anything to wipe it from his lips. "Oh wait. My bad," he mocks. "We already have."

"What I did or didn't do last night is none of your goddamn business—"

"Sweet, angelic Callahan still thinks he can do no wrong," Ford says.

"More like the fuck-up who thinks he can do no wrong," Ledger says.

I stare at my brothers and hate the tightness in my chest. The gloves are off.

How can you love two people and hate them just as much?

How did we get here? How did so much change in six months? How did . . . "Fuck off, Ledger. The constant do-gooder, wanna-be-daddy thing you've got going gets old."

"And the pretty party boy routine does too," he deadpans. "Normalizing the morning hangover and trying to remember the name of the woman you're rolling out of bed beside has to be tiresome."

My smile is slow and menacing when I look at him and speak. "It's a hell of a lot better than learning how to adjust the stick up my ass so I can walk, although it seems you've mastered that just fine."

"Of course. Responsibility and dedication are what you'd consider a stick up my ass." He matches my smile and just stares at me with a cool, even temper.

One much like my father had.

And the sight of it hurts.

I knew this would happen. This fight. This confrontation. The manifestation of a jealousy I never created nor could control.

But here we are, gloving up for a fight that has been brewing for months.

Anticipation of it is what led me to the club last night and the Johnnie Walkers at the bar.

Now there is nowhere to run. No woman to get lost in. No alcohol to numb its ugliness.

They want a fight? I'll give it to them.

I shrug nonchalantly. "We all grieve in different ways."

"Is that what you call this?" Ledger snorts, and all I can do short of walking out of here is grit my teeth. I shake my head and try to fight the anger mixed with pain raging through me. "Because I call it doing exactly what you've always done—*fucking off.* The difference? Dad's no longer here to protect you from the consequences."

"Is that why I was told I had to be here, *or else?* So you can put me in my place and assert some kind of power over me?" I lift a middle finger at them.

"You were told to be here because it's time for you to do your goddamn job."

"According to you, my job is fucking random women and sullying the Sharpe name. Is that what we're aiming for here? Because if that's the case, I'm all in."

"Typical." He shakes his head, and I swear to God it's déjà vu. He could be our father standing there with the high demands and lack of empathy for others. But there will be no phone call later telling me he understands and still loves me. *Like Dad did.* There will simply be more of the empty silence edged in resentment. *God, I miss him.*

"When did you start becoming our father?"

"When he died and you never stepped up to the plate to fulfill your duties."

"I'm here, aren't I?" I say, hands out to my sides, the disappointment I was trying to drink away last night is now staring me down through my brothers' eyes.

"Ah. Yes," Ledger says. "It's amazing how you'll drag your ass in here when threatened with a no-confidence vote from the board."

"*What did you say?*"

"You heard me."

I shove up out of my chair and force myself to walk to the windows instead of throw the punch I so desperately want to throw. A rage I never had before our dad died eats at me in a way I can't explain.

They want to vote me out?

My brothers, my blood, want me gone?

Hurt suffocates me, but I shove it behind a mask of zero fucks. Isn't that what I've always done? Move, dodge, weave, when shit gets too real?

Especially with my dad. Even with my brothers.

"Actually, I didn't hear you." My fists clench and my mind buzzes. "You want the board to vote me out?"

"You made your bed, brother. It's up to you if you want to lie in it or prove you deserve the position."

"So that's what this is all about, then?" I give a disbelieving shake of my head. "All that power is going to your head, Ledger."

"Maybe if you were around more, you'd know what the actual fuck was going on," Ledger states.

"Hey, Ledge?" I lean forward, lower my voice, and taunt him. "Sounds to me like you're the one who needs to use the suite. To get fucked. Maybe if you blow off some steam, dominate in the bedroom a little, it'll ease your need to—"

"This isn't a joke," he bellows, slamming his hand on the table.

"And neither is you threatening to kick me out of a company my goddamn name is on."

"*Our name, Callahan.* Not just yours." Ford glances over to Ledger and then back to me. "We've been busting our asses for the past six months trying to keep all the plates spinning and fill the void Dad left. *And you?* You've been nowhere to be found. You walked away from jobs half done, from deals half made. You fucking vanished to go have a pity party. Well guess what? He was our dad too, but we didn't get to leave. We didn't get to walk away from the responsibility that is paying your paycheck. So you're goddamn right we're pissed. You sit on your ass, collecting the same salary we do. We're sick of it. You're either part of this company and pulling your weight or you're out."

I hate that they have a valid point. I *did* leave. *But . . . I also hate their logic.* And what it means.

"So, *pulling my weight* to you means sending me to the failing resort and expecting me to turn it around? Ignoring that it's a shitty economy and that the resort needs a major overhaul?" *Fuck.* "You're setting me up to fail." *How did we get to this point?*

"Isn't that the same thing you did to us?" Ford asks. "Set us up to fail when you walked away?"

Motherfucker.

I stare at my brothers and all I see is my dad. *And feel the brutality of his absence.*

"You backed him on taking this deal when we opposed it," Ledger says.

"The majority owner of this company at the time wanted to buy the property, and I encouraged him to do what he wanted."

"The majority owner—*Dad*—was old with the beginning stages of dementia. The owner was trying to screw him. I saw it. Ford saw it. Christ, our lawyers saw it. But you were so goddamn occupied with trying to close the deal so you could fuck the owner's daughter that you didn't care." Another fist on the table and Ledger steps into me so that we are chest to chest. "You were supposed to protect him, Callahan. Protect us. Protect the fucking company. But you didn't. Now we have a resort that closed escrow a month after Dad died and it's been failing ever since. So yes, you're goddamn right this is your fault."

They weren't there.

They don't know.

And even when I've tried to explain it to them, they don't understand.

"Always thinking the worst of me. Right, Ledge?"

"As of late? Yes." He nods. His eyes are pained, upset about what has transpired, but not regretful. "But we're not Dad, Cal. We love you, but we're not blinded by your bullshit. We won't look the other way and make excuses for you."

I move to the wall of windows, hands shoved in my pockets, and stare at the nameless, faceless people below and wish I were one of them right now.

They want me to fail. To kick me out.

Isn't this what I wanted? To be free from the burden of being a Sharpe? To pick a dot on a map and go there and explore? Hell, I don't need the money—none of us do—as our accounts are large enough to live ten lavish lives on . . . so tell them to fuck off, Cal. Tell them *you win.* Tell them . . .

I can't.

This was *our dad's.* He built it from the ground up and as much as world domination isn't in my blood like it is in theirs, I can't walk away just yet.

This is the only piece of him I have left. *How dare they use it as an ultimatum?*

I'm damned if I do—flip the resort and be miserable in the process. And I'm damned if I don't—fail at turning it around and lose all that I've known. My brothers aren't going to change from self-righteous assholes, even if I stay for this fight.

"You wanted me back. *In person.* Hands-on. You've got me back." I look at both of them as I try to figure out how this happened to us. How our dad's death six months ago caused this huge divide. "I'll go down there. I'll see what the issue is. Then again, maybe I won't. But you'll have someone there with the Sharpe name so you can rest easier at night." I emit a sarcastic chuckle, take a grape off the fruit platter in the middle of the table, and pop it in my mouth. "Be careful what you wish for."

I make my way toward the doors, toward freedom, but his words stop me dead in my tracks.

"And here we thought you'd want to step up, that you'd want to honor Dad's memory, by making the last thing he bought with your blessing, thrive." Ledger tsks. "Clearly you don't fucking care."

I don't turn around. Can't. It hurts just looking at them. At seeing the bits and pieces of my father in them. The parts I never fucking got.

Maybe that's why I haven't been around.

Maybe that's why it's better to get that adrenaline rush than to waste my days in a goddamn suit and office with the one-hundred-eighty-degree view of Manhattan.

"I'll forgive you for saying that. Just this once." It's all I say before I storm out of the office.

Fuck it.

Fuck them.

Fuck my dad for dying.

I'll go to the Virgin Islands. I'll go because they think I won't. I'll figure out what the fuck is wrong with Ocean's Edge and make it better solely in memory of Maxton Sharpe. And when I'm done, I'll walk away from this fucking company and live the life my dad never got to because he was so busy working.

I refuse to allow Sharpe International to own me.

I refuse to allow anyone to own me.

CHAPTER EIGHT

Sutton

"I T'S PARADISE, LIZZY. ABSOLUTE PARADISE DISGUISED IN DATED décor that most definitely has to go and staff who need a pick-me-up in the friendly department."

"That's what my girl is there for," she shouts into the phone. "To kick ass, take names, and make that bitch profitable!"

Everybody needs a friend like Lizzy. The truth teller when you don't want to hear it and your biggest cheerleader when you need it even more. And the woman who stands guard at your apartment, looking to see if your ex comes home while you pack all of the clothing you need as quickly as possible.

"That's the plan," I say as I look around. Palm trees sway in the breeze and a steel drum can be heard playing somewhere in the distance. The crystal-clear ocean water and white sand beach is laid out in front of me in all its glory.

Beaches definitely don't look like this in New York.

Neither do resorts.

Where Manhattan is all sleek high-rises, miles of concrete, and a fast-paced energy, Ocean's Edge is exactly the opposite. The white clapboard buildings, while weathered and worn, sprawl across lush grounds where tropical plants and vibrant flowers dot every walkway and corner. The vibe is laid-back and serene.

Even in the short time I've wandered about, I can see why the Sharpe brothers bought this place. It's dog-eared and dated but the potential to make this a high-end concept is endless.

"So tell me about your room? Is it overlooking the water? Does it have a bird's-eye view of some hot, sexy gardener who refuses to wear a shirt because it's so hot, and who offers to trim your bush for free?"

"You're delusional."

"No, I'm stuck in New York while you're about to live your best life in paradise." She laughs. "So? Your room?"

"It's incredible." I sigh. "It's on the backside of the property—staff quarters, I assume—so no ocean views because those are reserved for the guests, but it's perfect in every other way. Open windows with ocean breezes and the sound of the palm trees rustling. It's perfect."

"Sounds heavenly, but what exactly does *staff quarters* mean? You're sharing a room with someone you don't know? That could put a damper on the abundance of sex you're going to have."

"Yes. That was my exact thought." I snort. "It's more like I have my own bed and bathroom and it opens into a common area with a kitchenette that I share with whoever occupies the other suite. Kind of like a two-bedroom apartment."

"And so, who occupies the other suite?"

"I'm not sure. I didn't even have time to look because I was delayed getting my rental car. I literally dropped off my stuff and headed out to my first meeting."

"And that went well?"

"It didn't happen at all because it was rescheduled for later tonight. Can't say I complained though because it gave me some time to sit back and enjoy this place before I jump in feet first tomorrow."

"You? Sit back and relax? Are you feeling okay?"

"As a matter of fact, I am. I currently have a rum punch in my hand—with a paper umbrella in it, I might add—and my toes are in the sand."

"Wow. I'm impressed. Like *really* impressed."

"I'm trying," I say, my voice softening as I lift my face to the sun, close my eyes, and let it warm my cheeks.

"I know you are. Dare I ask if you've heard anything from Clint yet to dampen this new place you're in?"

I emit a resigned chuckle. "Of course I have, but it hasn't changed my mind. He texted to see if I'd pick up his blue and yellow tie from the cleaners for him as well as a reminder to make sure I have the black dress with the cut-out neckline ready for dinner with his boss."

"So he's still in denial then."

"I don't think it's denial. It's more . . . self-righteousness? Arrogance? I don't even know what to call it, but he's in for a rude awakening when I'm not there for dinner with his boss."

"You promise?" Lizzy asks cautiously.

"Did you forget I'm hundreds of miles away now? It's over, Lizzy. Like over, over. I'm not going back, and I don't have any regrets other than the time I've wasted. I think I mistook duty for love and that's on me."

She lets her silence be her no-judgment answer, and for that I'm more than grateful.

Clint thinks I'll be going back because I can't live without him.

He's wrong. *Dead wrong.*

And the night of our breakup, the one-night stand that awakened all of my senses and the days following where I've thrown myself into the details of this project without pause, proved just how wrong he was.

Besides, ending a two-year relationship should entail some sadness and grief, not relief and regret.

I think that says enough in and of itself.

"I'm so proud of you," she murmurs, causing my carefree smile to widen.

"*This* is one hundred percent what I need right now. Some time away. A new job to focus on. A new experience to enjoy. The—"

"The triplet you want to fuck again."

"I—uh—"

"Cat got your tongue? Because you know I'm right."

"More like cat's got my tongue because sometimes the things you say are shocking."

"Having to work with a man who might or might not be the man who fucked your brains out is shocking. Having to work with a man who looks exactly like the man who dirty-talked you into oblivion and not being able to think of anything else while he discusses staff salary structures and guest complaints is even worse. I mean, you're damned if

63

it's him and you're damned if it isn't. Maybe the solution is you ask for a triplet sandwich and be done with it."

"There is something sooooo wrong with you." I laugh and draw a look from a woman passing by.

"You know you've already thought of it. What sane woman wouldn't have?"

"Perhaps." A smile creeps onto my lips. "But nothing is going to happen. No sleeping with my boss. No triplet sandwiches. No anything." And just the thought has my thighs clenching together.

This is not a good sign.

"Callahan." She draws the name out as if she didn't hear a word I said. "That's a mouthful. Do you think he'll let you shorten it to Cal in the heat of passion? *Oh Cal, give me your monster cock, baby.*"

"Jesus. This isn't even a topic we're discussing. Sleeping with my boss is a line I can't cross. I have too much to lose."

Her suggestive laugh has me rolling my eyes. "Then I guess it's going to be a one-way discussion, honey, because I'm talking about it."

My sigh fills the line, but my smile she can't see widens.

"I believe your words were *the best sex you'd ever had,*" she continues. "Earth-shattering was another adjective. You didn't think anyone would ever compare was another description. I don't know about you, but that kind of sex is worth breaking the rules over."

"In any other situation, yes. *Maybe.*" I look around to make sure no one is within earshot of my side of the conversation.

Maybe.

Why did I even say that? There is no *maybe* about sleeping with my boss.

"I can't risk this opportunity, Lizzy. I have too much riding on it. And for what? Good sex with a guy who is clearly the poster boy for One-Night Stand 101? I mean, I'm more than certain the shock I felt walking into that conference room was tenfold for him. While I've never done something like that before, clearly he has."

"There is no shame to be had on either side of that equation."

"No, but if he wanted my number to get to know me better or was interested in going out again, he would have left me a card or woken me up before he left. He didn't. That tells me where I stand. It was one and done and that's fine."

"So you're totally fine sitting beside and working day in and day out with a man who rocked your world?"

"It might not be him."

"Correct, but if it is . . . are you telling me that there won't be that tug there? Those *kitty* butterflies every single time you brush a hand against his or he looks at you a certain way?"

"This is a moot point. Let's say Callahan *is* Johnnie. Since he's had several days with my phone number in hand and still hasn't called, it doesn't matter if I get kitty butterflies or not, clearly the chase is over and he's no longer interested in me."

"You could always talk him into sex without strings. Sex for the sake of sex. Sex as a means to relax after a long, frustrating day. Sex as—"

"I get the point," I say and shift in my seat, my mind replaying the sight of him standing between my thighs, his hand stroking his cock. "But like I said, Callahan might not be Johnnie."

"But what if he is . . ."

"One—"

"Oh God, she's counting." Lizzy laughs. "That means you're about to lay down the law for me."

I chuckle and start again. "One, you're assuming I want to have sex with him again."

"You do."

I do.

"Maybe he was a unicorn. Maybe you only ride a unicorn once because it's magical and never meant to be had again."

"A unicorn? God help me."

"Two. Callahan might not have been Johnnie. So, then what? I ask him and then blow my cover that I've already slept with one of his brothers? I mean . . . that doesn't exactly bode well for me in the keeping my job department."

"True, but—"

"And three, if Callahan is Johnnie and he wanted to smooth things over with me before I got here, he's known where to reach me. All he had to do was call and straighten things out. A quick, *this is awkward, but it won't affect my professionalism or the job you have to do for us.* Or even, *it was great, and what happened will stay between us.* It could even be, *I'm Johnnie. The other night was incredible, and I want to see you again.* But my phone hasn't rung, and that leads me to believe that he doesn't want me to know which one he was. He holds all the cards right now. I can't force him to play his hand."

And I'm not one hundred percent sure how I feel about that. Rejected but relieved. Unsettled but resolute.

Or just plain crazy.

I vote for the latter.

"Point taken."

"And four? He's my boss. I can't sleep with him. It'll only serve to muddy up the waters when I have this huge opportunity for me at work."

"I hear you," she murmurs, "but I'm still holding out hope for some wild monkey sex."

"Great. I'm glad someone is."

CHAPTER NINE

Callahan

MY EYES BURN AND MY HEAD IS MUSH WITH ALL THE FIGURES and feedback and who the fuck knows what that I've tried to acquaint myself with over the past forty-eight hours.

It's been a while since I've had to really concentrate on crap like this, and now I remember why I've avoided it. *It's soul-sapping shit.* The kind of shit that you could interpret seven different ways depending on the day and your mood.

But hell if Ledger's words didn't eat at me after I left the conference room.

I got drunk, shitfaced really, while replaying every word of that god-damn argument in my head.

In particular, the ones telling me if I really wanted to honor our dad, I should do it by making his last decision shine. Taking this mediocre resort and turning it around into a luxury resort like our other S.I.N. properties.

And then I drank some more. To bury the grief over the loss of my father. To feed the fury over my brothers' threats and suppositions. To dampen the desire to call Sutton and fuck her again.

All three felt valid and important.

All three still do.

And yet when I woke up with a wicked hangover, I resolved to get my shit together.

I'd go to the resort. I'd turn shit around as fast as I could, then walk away to that dot on a map where I could fall off the grid. Oh, and I'd keep my hands off Sutton.

The last one was my least favorite of the three by far.

But isn't that what Ledger and Ford expect of me? To spend way too much time pursuing her—or some other piece of ass—and not do my job?

So fuck if I'm not here, elbow deep in spreadsheets and managers' reports, stuck inside this office with paradise taunting me outside the open window, trying to get up to speed before my meeting with Sutton and the resort's manager, Brady, in a few minutes.

Sutton.

Shit.

Talk about a clusterfuck of epic proportions.

I can't sleep with her, can I? Isn't that what I told myself? That if I was going to do this, I was going to do it wholeheartedly even at the expense of my own goddamn pleasure.

It's fucking cruel to her. Keeping her wondering, guessing if I'm *him*. Johnnie Walker. But isn't that the best for both of us? If she doesn't know then it's cleaner that way. Her feelings can't be hurt. Things will have to remain platonic.

So . . . no. There will be no sex. No touchy-feely. No fucking anything. Just constant reminders of every damn minute I spent buried inside her.

But how do you keep your hands off the best sex of your life?

There. I said it. *She was.* It was. And I haven't stopped thinking about it or her since I walked out of the suite that morning.

I can tell myself she was a one-night stand, that we both knew it walking up to the suite that night, and so keeping it to myself that I was the guy isn't really that big of a deal. She wouldn't have known who I was if we'd never met again, so why should it be any different now?

The problem is me.

I want her again.

I fucking can't stop thinking about her or her body or that soft little moan that would escape just as her orgasm slammed into her.

What man wouldn't?

"Shit," I mutter as I start over at the top of the report for the tenth time, my cock hardening at just the thought of her.

I see a lot of jerking off in my future.

That same thought echoes in my mind a few minutes later as I walk across the sprawling landscape of Ocean's Edge to The Cove, the resort's high-end restaurant, where I rescheduled for us to have our meeting. Maybe I should have stolen away to the villa to do just that first. Get off thinking about her so that when I do come face-to-face with her, when I do smell that subtle scent she wears on her skin, I don't get hard immediately.

I've never had this problem before. The urge to have seconds. The need to have more. *Or even the want to.*

I step into the restaurant, my laptop and some loose-leaf folders under my arm, and check out my surroundings. The first time in person. It's rich in colors with dark woods and dim lights to set the ambiance and not take away from the real showstopper—the ocean lapping up against its patio.

I take in the guests. By all accounts, their clothing and jewelry telegraph to me that they're middle class. Not the ones who will spend the big bucks but the ones who have scraped together enough money to say they went to the Virgin Islands but couldn't spend the cash on the activities to make the trip worth it.

Ugly as the truth may be, these are not the guests the S.I.N. brand looks for. We want the upper class. The elite. The guests who don't give a second thought when they set down their American Express Black card to buy souvenirs or clothes from the many shops we have on-site or buy all the tickets to a group excursion so they have privacy for themselves. They're the ones we can raise prices on, and they won't bat an eye at them.

Quick appraisal done; I head down the hallway to the back room where our meeting is being held. I thought a nice dinner meeting with Sutton and our resort manager would be a good way to break the ice.

Having a third party present would help prevent me from breaking the promise I made to myself in telling Sutton who I am.

"Excuse me," a soft voice murmurs from behind me when I stop to make note of a few changes that need to be made to the interior of the restaurant.

"Sorry." I step out of the way and turn to offer a smile in apology to the woman. She falters in her step when her eyes lock with mine. She's tall with auburn hair and an incredible body, but it's her slow crawl of a smile and appraising gaze that tells me I could have her with minimal effort.

"Not a problem at all. My table is that way." She points to her right and gives me another look before walking down the hallway toward her table.

I stare for a beat and wonder if this is the answer to my problem. Finding another woman to help dim the taste of Sutton on my tongue and the imprint she left on my mind.

Fuck to forget. That's a new concept for me because forgetting is typically easy, but it's plausible and definitely feasible.

And just as quickly as the idea cements in my mind, it vanishes when I look up and see her sitting there.

Sutton Pierce.

Jesus Christ.

The woman is stunning. There's no other way to describe her other than absolutely stunning.

I give myself the moment to study her as she talks to the maître d'. Her hair is pulled back into a soft, messy bun at the nape of her neck with loose pieces falling around her face. She has on a muted yellow tank top with silver bands lining one of her wrists. Her smile is soft and her eyes warm as she carries on the conversation.

Who the hell is this woman and why can't I stop staring at her?

"Callahan. You finally got off the tarmac, I see." I turn to find Brady, the resort manager, standing beside me with a big smile and an extended hand.

"I did." I shake his hand, my attention shifting to the man before me. He's tall and lanky with salt and pepper hair and a genuine smile.

"And luckily the skies cleared up to give us this beautiful sunset for your first evening here with us."

"Lucky me," I murmur as we move into the room.

"Gentlemen," Sutton says. "Great to finally have some time to sit down and discuss with you how we can make this resort not only more inviting, but more importantly, more profitable."

"Music to my ears," Brady says.

For the first time Sutton turns to face me. Her smile is wide and her eyes searching. Our gazes hold for the slightest of seconds, and I wonder if she's figured it out.

"Sutton," I say with a nod to try and prevent her from looking too closely.

"Good to see you again, Mr. Sharpe."

"Callahan, please."

"Yes. Of course." She motions toward the table for us to sit. "I look forward to the chance to show you exactly what I can do."

I almost groan at the double entendre, my body knowing the answer to that question already.

This pretending thing is going to be much harder than I anticipated.

And so the meeting begins. First impressions about Ocean's Edge are the topic of conversation during appetizers. Guest expectations and how we are failing them are what we discuss during the starter salads. Budget projections and staff issues our focus over our entrees.

The conversation is akin to watching paint dry—dull and boring— and I keep having to remind myself that I'm better off if I don't look at Sutton.

It's easier on the dull ache thrumming at the base of my balls.

"Clearly there's a long list of items to cover in the timeframe we've been allotted, so how do we do this?" Sutton asks.

We walk back to your room. We find the nearest surface—or floor. And we fuck until we can't walk.

When I shake the thought, both of them are looking at me. "Oh. Yes. Sorry. I was lost in the details." I offer a quick smile. "Should we enjoy an after-dinner drink while we discuss the how-tos?" They both look at each other tentatively as, technically, I'm their boss asking if they want to drink while on the job. "I assure you, this isn't a test. We're going to be working together a lot over the coming months. It's just a drink to celebrate, if you will."

"Sure," Brady says. "That would be nice."

"Fine. Yes," Sutton says as I motion to the waiter who's standing nearby, well aware who we are and that our needs need to be met.

"Sir?" the waiter asks.

"We'd like some drinks. The lady will have a—"

"Tom Collins," we both say at the same time.

Sutton gasps.

Oh fuck.

"Actually," Sutton starts, "no Tom Collins for me." Her eyes bore into mine as I cringe at my mistake. *Motherfucker.* "I appreciate you ordering for me, *Callahan*, but I've found that I've rather gone off its taste if I'm honest."

"I hate that," Brady interjects, having no clue what he's stepping into. "It's usually after a night of overindulging that I fall off my usual for a bit." He turns to the waiter, oblivious to the fire in Sutton's eyes. "I'll have an old fashioned."

Sutton purses her lips, gaze locked on mine. "Exactly, Brady. Nothing like the taste of a favorite drink being soured." *She's pissed? At me?* She turns to the waiter. "I'll have a Negroni, please."

Fucking A. She *is* pissed. What the actual fuck?

"And you, sir?"

CHAPTER TEN

Sutton

"Johnnie Walker Blue, please. My usual," Callahan says, never once breaking his hold on my gaze. *What. The. Hell.* Callahan is Johnnie? And he's known all this time. The shock that was painted on his face moments ago after his slip-up has now been replaced with a smirk that I can't figure out if it's a taunt or an invitation. But make no mistake, there was shock etched in the lines of his face. And if I'm reading his fingers suddenly tugging on the top button of his collar correctly, he definitely had no intention of letting me know. And yet, there is no shame in his expression, but rather a smugness that is as irritating as it is sexy. "I find I'm not one to change my ways regardless of the situation."

I purse my lips and give a subtle snort, more than aware from our conversation so far tonight that Brady is quite observant.

"Good to know," I murmur, trying to decipher what exactly Callahan means by his comment.

That he's not apologizing for what happened and will do it again with the next willing woman on the rebound?

Or did he like what happened and wants it to happen again? But is that want there only because he got caught? Only because of his slip of the tongue?

There definitely were no complaints about his tongue.

Seriously? That's where my thoughts go as my crossed legs squeeze a little tighter.

All this talk about *I won't be sleeping with him because he's my boss* and at the first affirmation that Callahan is in fact *him*, my mind immediately goes to his many . . . um, *skills*.

I fist my hands in anger. At me for thinking this way. At him for thinking he can just let a bomb drop like that—a bomb he was clearly holding on to until he felt it served his purpose or benefit—and that I'd be utterly okay with it.

Well, I'm not.

And what pisses me off more is I'm not sure why. I knew going into that night what it was, so what changed along the way? It shouldn't matter if I have to work with him or not, because it wasn't like I was ever going to see him again anyway.

So, is it the fact that he dropped that bomb and then gave me a cocky smirk as if he were so good that I'd bat my lashes and drop my panties at the mere acknowledgment that he's Johnnie?

Not on his life.

At least that's what I keep telling myself as the ache within me smolders to life when he runs his fingertip absently around the rim of his glass.

Those fingers.

Those hands.

That mouth.

Stop thinking about it. About him. You can't. Simply put.

You. Can't.

He's your boss.

He. Is. Your. Boss.

And not only is he your boss, but he's currently throwing you off center when you need to be at the top of your game to pull this resort transformation off.

I draw in a deep breath to reset.

"So," Brady says, looking back and forth between the two of us, no doubt trying to figure out why there is so much tension all of a sudden. "Shall we continue then?"

"Yes. Of course." I smile and quirk a brow. "What are your thoughts on everything, Callahan? You've been rather quiet. This is a Sharpe property, after all. Certainly you must have some thoughts or ideas on how to improve the experience for our guests."

"Are we talking about retention here or the overall experience?" he asks.

"I think both are rather important," Brady says.

"Agreed," I add. "Then let's focus on the experience portion first."

"What about it?" Callahan asks. "For some of our guests, this is an experience they've never had before. For others, heading to a tropical resort is something they do often."

"So it's nothing special to them then? Just another trip among many other trips?" I ask without thinking.

"You'd hope for the experience to be special for both sets of people, but nothing is ever guaranteed," Callahan says, angling his head to the side when his eyes meet mine.

"Clearly," I murmur.

"Besides the obvious," Brady says glancing at the notes he'd taken, "like better amenities and excursions, new menu items and upgrading the overall décor so it's not so dated, how do we know if they'll come back or not?"

"Retention," I state.

"Coming back for more," Callahan rephrases my words, and I swear he's doing this to goad me. And if his words weren't enough, the look in his eyes confirms it.

Two can play at this game.

"What about a follow-up call after they leave? Some communication. A means to let them know that even though the vacation is now over, that it *and them* were in fact valued while they experienced it?" I ask.

"What about those people who made it clear from the get-go—you know, the ones who didn't check the box that said they agreed to being added to the mailing list or some bullshit like that? They don't want added communication after they leave," Callahan says with a shrug. "They just want to remember the experience for what it's worth instead of messing up the memory by rehashing it."

"I hardly think a phone call asking if they enjoyed their stay is messing up the memory," I state, feathers more than ruffled.

"I agree with you on this, Sutton," Brady says and then grimaces as he looks from Callahan to me and then back to Callahan as he tries to weigh how Callahan will react since he is in fact, his boss. "But I mean . . ."

"The bonus factor to making the phone call is the caller could ask the guest if there was anything we could have done to make their experience better," I say.

"Make their experience better?" Callahan repeats absently.

I nod, fighting my smirk. That one got his attention. "Yes. Even the best experiences could use some improvement. It's arrogant of the host to think they're . . . flawless."

"I like that idea," Brady says. "The operator could go down a check sheet with questions . . ."

But I don't hear the rest of what he says because when I turn my attention from Brady to Callahan, he is looking right at me with a crooked smirk on that gorgeous face of his. The only person at this table still talking about Ocean's Edge is Brady because it's clear neither Callahan nor I are.

"I'm not in disagreement," Callahan finally acquiesces even though I know it pains him to. And I feel the slightest victory because of it. "But I'm also of the mind that we make their experience so incredible the first time around that a phone call isn't needed to remind them of the memory."

"But a phone call still would be nice," I say with a saccharine-sweet smile. "To let them know they were valued regardless of whether we ever see them again or not. Common courtesy and all that."

"Common courtesy and all that," Callahan murmurs before taking a sip of his drink, his eyes meeting mine just above its rim.

"I think that's a good start," Brady says with a resolute nod. "We at least have a general roadmap to start with. From there we can dig down to the nitty-gritty details as we go."

"Agreed," I say, more than confused about what Callahan was trying to say to me with all the comments.

But I think I gave as good as I got.

At least I hope I did.

"Callahan? Is there anything further on your agenda you'd like to discuss tonight?"

That smirk is back. This time it's followed by a soft chuckle. "Not at this time. I think we have many nights to discuss the intricacies of how we make our guests come back for seconds."

"Very true. Of course, the ultimate goal would be a carryover to other properties you own," Brady suggests, clearly trying to make up for his agreement with me. "We just need to ask ourselves the question: how do we entice them to want to use Sharpe International resorts exclusively?"

I give a nod to Brady. "I'm fairly certain that if they should stumble across a *sibling* property, their first taste here will encourage them to try the others out." I look directly at Callahan and shrug, my expression stoic. "I mean, why limit yourself to just one Sharpe resort when there are others you could experience? Who knows, you might be better suited for a different one. While they all might have the same look, each one has differing attributes. Everyone loves to have options."

Callahan's grip on his glass is so tight his knuckles are white.

Good.

Serves him right.

CHAPTER ELEVEN

Callahan

SHE TAUNTED ME.

Sat there and fucking taunted me with her bullshit comments about how one should experience *other Sharpes* and see which one fits the best. Then she excused herself from the table with a smirk and said she had to review a few more things before she went to bed.

What the hell was that all about?

But I'm the one who slipped, fucking showed my cards, when I hadn't planned on it. I was so damn preoccupied with not being affected by her, or rather not letting her know I was affected by her, that I wasn't thinking clearly.

Then I spent the rest of our bizarre battle of wills grasping for straws as I tried to put her off me. Piss her off and think that I didn't want anything more with her than the night in the suite to make it easier for me to push her away. To not act on the desire that thrummed in my veins each and every time our eyes met.

The irony? I didn't want more than that night with her. The sex was incredible but like always, when I shut that door and walked away, for all intents and purposes, I was over it. Over her.

Wasn't that the whole point? A rebound. Sex without strings. No regrets.

But clearly I wasn't over her.

Not when I ordered her Starbucks. Certainly not when she walked her fine ass out of the conference room to leave me picking my jaw up off the floor and adjust the hard-on in my pants. And definitely not now that we're stuck working together over the next few months. It's going to be one long, miserable stretch to want someone and not be able to act on it.

You promised that you wouldn't, Callahan.

The woman has moxie, that's for sure.

And why is it such a turn-on?

Fuck me and my promises.

I stand with my hands on my hips staring into the moonlit night. I don't see the flames of the tiki torches or white clapboard fronts of the buildings. I don't hear the steel drums or smell the scent of the ocean. I don't even know that I'm in paradise because right now I'm sitting in my own personal hell.

All I can think about is that little tug of war we just had in front of Brady. All I can focus on is the sound of her soft laugh and the defiance and challenge in her eyes.

Needs improvement, my ass.

The woman is definitely something else. Doing something that most can't—push my buttons.

My phone rings. *Ledger.* Just what I fucking need.

We've yet to discuss the other day but in classic Sharpe form, we won't. We'll brush everything under the goddamn rug and pretend like it never happened.

So that means he's only calling for one thing.

I roll my shoulders and am grateful this time around I've had a drink before I talk to him.

"Ledger." No niceties. He doesn't deserve it.

"Are you fucking kidding me?" He laughs the question out.

"What am I missing here?" I move a few feet outside of the walk-way to have some privacy.

"You've been there one day and you've already cancelled your first meeting? Christ, Callahan. Couldn't you at least try?"

Every part of me tenses—my jaw, my fists, my shoulders—and yet when I speak, my voice holds that aloofness that I know for certain pisses him off. "Ah, and I thought you weren't keeping tabs on me."

"Earn the right for me not to, and I won't."

Has he been drinking? It's not like him to tie one on in the middle of the week. "What do you want, Ledge?"

"Same thing I've always wanted. For you to man the fuck up and do your part. Par for the course, you're not." He emits a sarcastic chuckle. "How were we ever from the same father?"

His words hit me like a battering ram. We have our differences, our father's differing treatment of each of us being the main thing, but he's still my brother. Still my best friend. Or . . . was. Every part of me riots against the words he just said.

"I'm going to pretend I didn't just hear you say that, brother," I say between gritted teeth. "And then we're going to start this conversation over before you really piss me off and I block you from my phone so that you can't call and treat me like a child yet again." I draw in a deep breath. "So, what is it that I can do for you?"

"Stop playing these bullshit games. You're there to work, to set an example for the staff of what's expected, not fuck around like a rich playboy."

"Back the fuck off, Ledge," I warn.

"Why? You're going to keep doing what you do, and I'll keep doing what I do."

"So that's how it's going to go?"

"Apparently."

"Then maybe you should check Silas's flight log," I say, referring to the pilot of the company's private jet. "It'll tell you that I was stuck on the tarmac during the scheduled meeting because of lightning from a sudden thunderstorm that passed over the island. Sixty-six minutes sitting on the tarmac to be exact. And so I rescheduled the meeting that took place about two hours ago and just finished, not that I have to explain myself to you or anything." Fucking hell. I walk from one side of the clearing to the other. "I love you, Ledger, but I don't exactly like you right now."

"Now you know how I've felt on and off over the past fifteen years since Mom died."

The dig is there. Not even subtle. Not even anything. Just there out in the open.

I have nothing more to say to him so I end the call without another word.

The darkened ocean stretches out before me, its waves lapping against the shore, but I clench my jaw so tightly that my teeth hurt.

Fuck. I'm so damn sick of this shit.

A light turns on in a villa near me and the silhouette of a woman passes in front of the curtained window. I stare absently at her as my frustrated desire comes back riding shotgun next to my fury at my brother.

My feet move without thought. There is only one thing I want right now. One person who can give that to me.

I kept the promise for twenty-four hours. That's longer than most attempts. At least I'm making progress.

Hell, if I'm going to be accused of being the black sheep, I might as well earn the title.

CHAPTER TWELVE

Sutton

"DISTANCE IS GOOD," I MUTTER TO MYSELF AS I PULL ON MY camisole. "Space is good." Then slip on my flimsy sleep shorts. "Not looking at him or studying his hands or smelling his cologne is even better."

Because that was hard enough tonight.

I glance up to see my reflection in the floor-length mirror opposite my bed. My dark brown hair is piled on top of my head in a messy bun and my face is newly scrubbed of my makeup. "You sound crazy, Sutt." Batshit crazy to be exact.

But the arrogant, sexy man is under my skin, and it doesn't appear he'll be leaving any time soon.

The solution? Some more wine—definitely—and getting lost in a million more reports until my brain is so tired, I have no option other than to fall asleep without a thought of one Callahan Sharpe. *Hopefully.*

I open my bedroom door and head out to do just that, my thoughts on how I need to book a mani-pedi at the resort's spa on my next free time to check out the facilities, when I look up. "Fuck."

And that one, startled word is met with the quirk of a lone eyebrow of one Callahan Sharpe. He is sitting in a chair that's facing my bedroom door in the common area of the villa, legs spread casually, elbow on one of its arms with a glass of what I can presume is whiskey in his hand. He still has his dark slacks on from earlier and his dress shirt is now open another button at the neck.

But it's the look on his face that owns my attention. Intense. A little dangerous. Focused.

"What are you doing here? How did you get in? Callahan—"

"I own the resort." He holds the key card up in his other hand, stare unwavering. "I have access to any room I want."

I should be unnerved by the comment . . . but dare I say I'm a little turned on by it? Or maybe it's just him in general that turns me on. Regardless, he's here in my villa, dominating the decent-sized space with his presence when I'm trying desperately not to be affected by him.

"And you chose to use that all-access power to come to my room."

His shrug reeks of arrogance. "I wanted to see you again."

"Why?"

His eyes flicker down to my breasts beneath my tank top, take in my nipples pressed against the white, flimsy fabric, and then come back up to meet mine. "Because I'm a masochist."

"Clearly," I say nonchalantly and move toward my glass of wine on the counter. A drink is in order, for certain. "But you've already made your case with all of the things you did and didn't say tonight."

He takes a sip himself, his gaze moving to the glass in his hand. "And what exactly did I say?" Amber eyes meet mine and challenge.

"You know what? Never mind." I take a step back and give a soft chuckle knowing this is dangerous territory. Apparently, everything is when it comes to him. "Let's ignore the meeting tonight. What happened between us the other night. Just everything. I think we'll be better off for it if we do."

"You're a hard one to ignore, Collins." His eyes all but fuck me.

"It's Sutton."

"Whatever you say, Collins." He gives a ghost of a crooked smile. "Just one question though. How many times have you replayed that night in your mind? Did you slide your hand between your thighs when you did? Did you pretend it was me?" He shifts in his chair to adjust the hardening bulge between his thighs.

A glance is all I'll give him, even though the simple thought has my own body reacting.

"You didn't want me to know you were Johnnie. *Him*. That says enough for me to know how and what you thought of me."

"How and what I thought of you?" He gives a subtle nod. "We met at a club. We had rather incredible sex afterwards. Sex we both wanted. I wasn't aware there were whispered promises for more that I wasn't fulfilling."

I open my mouth to speak and then hesitate because everything he's saying is true. That doesn't mean he didn't have to be courteous. And honestly? I'm edging for a fight, for something, for anything to abate the sexual tension vibrating around us.

"You could have called so that we walked into this partnership on solid footing. You holding all the cards like I was some game to you was a dick move."

"The fact that you couldn't remember who you slept with isn't my problem."

"Excuse me?" I stumble over the words in disbelief.

"For the record, I'm better than my brothers."

Jesus. The fact that I didn't know it was him is eating at him. *Good.* At least something about this whole situation bugs him.

"Calling would have been a mistake," he continues when I don't speak.

"And why's that?"

"Because you would have ended up beneath me—or on top, I'm not picky—and I believe that would have been worse than me not calling."

I swear to God my nipples harden at his words. Words I don't want to be a slave to but that my body is nonetheless. "I'm not a plaything, Callahan. Especially not yours."

He emits a soft chuckle. "Oh, I'm aware."

"You weren't going to tell me you were Johnnie, were you?" He angles his head and stares, surprising me when he gives the subtlest of nods in response. "That says everything I need to know."

"Maybe I was trying to do the right thing," he murmurs.

"I have a feeling you don't think much about right or wrong most times, so why start now?" My words are out of my mouth before I even realize my thoughts have been voiced. They're a taunt to him. A challenge.

And I just opened the door for him to take it. For him to prove that right or wrong, if he wants me, he'll pursue me.

Isn't him sitting here in my villa proof of that?

I told myself I couldn't do this. That if Callahan was Johnnie, I'd have to keep my libido and desire on lockdown.

But now that I'm standing here in the lion's den, every bone in my body wants what I've told myself I can't have.

"There you go making assumptions again," he says.

I take a step closer. "I know you like to play with power. That's not an assumption."

"No?"

"Like I said, you had three days to pick up your phone and call me. To have us start out on a professional footing. You didn't. That says you wanted me on edge, not knowing. You wanted a toy you could bat around when you felt the need to play."

He moves for the first time, setting down his drink and rising from his chair. "I was going to forget you." He undoes one cuff on his shirt and folds the sleeve up his forearm. "I was going to let this play out so that you'd never know." And then the other cuff, my eyes transfixed on his fingers. "I thought I'd be able to resist you." He looks up and takes a step toward me. "But fucking hell, Sutton, I realized that would be an impossible feat when I saw you sitting at that table at dinner tonight."

He takes another step so that he's within a foot of me. Our eyes hold for a beat as he leans in and for a second, I think he's going to kiss me.

Every part of my body vibrates with a need I don't understand. I whisper, "I can't do this, Callahan."

His lips quirk. "I like hearing my name on your lips."

"Good. Great." I stumble over those two seemingly easy words and force myself to focus on the matter at hand, standing my ground, instead of remembering the way his lips tasted. "You'll hear it a lot. When we *work* together."

I take a step back, my ass hitting the table behind me, and I grip the edge of the table to prevent me from touching him. He takes one step forward and reaches out to play with a piece of loose hair that has fallen out of my bun. I steel myself for the whisper of touch but it still makes my breath hitch.

"I can't sleep with my boss. *With you.*"

"We wouldn't exactly be sleeping, Sutton."

"Then I can't *fuck* my boss. Is that better?"

He groans, the sound of it rumbling through the room. "Do you know how much it turns me on when you talk like that?"

When he dips down and brushes his lips over mine, I don't resist. *Can't.* Isn't this what I've been thinking about since that morning? Kissing him again? Tasting him again?

His tongue delves between my lips. He tastes like the whiskey he was just drinking and the man I've been craving.

My hands tense on the edge of the granite as he shifts the angle of the kiss and tries to coax more from me.

It feels so good it hurts in all the best ways possible. And just as I'm about to sink farther into the kiss, *into him,* my mind has a moment of clarity amid my body's betrayal of it.

"I can't." I move my head to the side and sit my butt on the table, scooting it back to gain some space. "I'm sorry. I promised myself this wouldn't happen. That I couldn't let it happen."

He scrubs a hand over his jaw, his amber eyes firing with desire. "Why not?" He runs one finger over the top of my thigh, his voice a low tenor. "It's hard to resist something when you want it so badly." This time he places both hands on the tops of my thighs and rubs his thumbs beneath my shorts. They rub back and forth so they just brush over the seam between my thighs. A soft moan falls from my lips in reflex. He watches me with every movement of his fingertips, and I fight to keep a stoic expression, but my pussy clenches at his touch, the ache it causes is so damn sweet. "And we both know you want it badly. You want *me* badly."

"Arrogant fuck," I mutter as I steel myself for another pass of his thumbs.

"Yes. *Please.*" He chuckles.

"Callahan. I can't."

"For a woman who doesn't want this, why are you pushing that sweet cunt of yours into my hand?" he taunts before leaning in and taking my bottom lip between his teeth and tugging ever so gently.

"I think this is the very definition of sexual harassment," I murmur as his thumb actually slides between my sex this time, finding the wetness of arousal there, before running back up and circling over my clit.

My body disobeys. It's ruled by his touch and not by the rationale in my head that seems to get foggier and foggier with each passing second.

"No. Me grabbing you and fucking you up against the wall like I desperately want to would be the definition of sexual harassment. *This?*" He groans the next four words out. "This is goddamn perfection."

"I thought I was just a one-night stand," I murmur. His cock hits my leg and I'm reminded just how hard and sizeable he is.

"Things change."

My breath hitches as his thumb presses just at my opening, my muscles tightening around him as if I'm desperate for his touch. He chuckles when he feels the involuntary response.

"Fuck me, Collins." He pushes his thumb deeper into me, and I fight having any kind of reaction with everything I have to try not to moan out in pleasure, because this isn't what's supposed to happen. I'm not supposed to give in to this. At least not without a better fight. His eyes meet mine again. "*That wasn't a request.*"

"You're assuming I want you again."

"I don't have to assume anything, *Collins*. You know you walked into that conference room the other day with a sore pussy and sat there with soaked panties as you wondered which one of us fucked you, because all you could think about was me doing it again." I cry out as he shifts so that he can tuck two fingers in me with one hand while unzipping his slacks with the other. My hands are still braced on the edge of the table, the only parts of our bodies that touch are where his fingers are.

I struggle to keep my wits and not be pulled under by the pleasure. For my mouth to not water at the sight of his beautiful cock ready and waiting to pleasure me.

But his arrogance taunts me. His assumption that he can enter my villa and I'd give him what he wants without question irritates me.

I need to regain my footing.

I choose to play with fire.

"I was certain it was Ledger." I pant the words out and then gasp when his fingers stop moving.

"What did you just say?"

"He seemed in control. Calculated. Dominant. If I had to guess," I lie, "I would have figured Ledger was the one."

Callahan stares at me, jaw tense and neck muscles taut, and emits a primal growl I don't even pretend to understand. He takes the hand off his cock, fists it in the back of my hair, and kisses me with a violent intensity that leaves me breathless.

And then he holds my head still as he looks at me, his fingers beginning to move and push and tease my nerves within me again.

"Rest assured, you'll know who exactly it was—who it is—the next time you're in a room with me and my brothers. Make no doubt, Collins."

"That remains to be seen," I taunt.

"Goddamn it," Callahan mutters as he works me into a frenzy. Sensations race through me.

One after another.

After another.

They chase the high until it slams into me with brute force. My toes tingle and my chest heaves as the aftereffects of pleasure wreak havoc on my body.

"Tell me I can fuck you," he grits out.

Do I really want to deny myself this? *Deny myself him?*

I can't think clearly with him in my space, with the post-orgasmic haze still wreaking havoc on my body, but I know I have something he wants.

And I know for the first time, I'm in a position of power.

"What's in it for me?"

"*What's in it for you?*" he asks as he releases the hold on my hair, takes a step back, and studies me as if he's confused by the question.

I bite my bottom lip and nod. "Hmm-mmm."

"Incredible sex," he says with a nonchalant shrug and stroke of his cock as if that's all I need to hear.

"That's not enough," I say as his eyes narrow. Clearly he has always been enough for anyone. "If I'm risking my job, there sure as hell better be something in this for me."

"You get this." He points to his cock and then where my sleep shorts have a wet stain on them. "Orgasms upon orgasms and sex with me."

"Like I said, that's not enough."

"What do you mean that's *not enough?*"

"What I said. You get caught with an employee, and you're still a Sharpe with a bank account you'll never be able to empty in your lifetime. If I get caught, I lose my job, my possible promotion, and given I'm counting on those things to help me pay for a place to live when I get back, I'm taking all the risks by sleeping with my boss. You're not."

"So what do you want? A job reference in case it happens? A guarantee that nothing's going to happen?" He looks so confused and it would be adorable if he wasn't standing there with his cock hard as a rock. "I'm not in the habit of giving things to get things."

"Clearly." My chuckle is low and throaty as I scoot off the counter and step toward him. He sucks in a breath when he thinks I'm going to kiss him, and much like he did, I move toward his ear and whisper, "For the record, I'll be offended if you think this is about money or advancement within your company. I want neither." *But I do want my pride. And I refuse to be available at his bidding. Powerless.*

"Then, what . . ." he says as I take a few steps toward my bedroom. "Where are you going?"

I turn and smile at him. "Giving you time to figure out the right answer, Callahan." I smirk, my body still tingling from my climax as I glance down to his cock and then back up to his eyes. "Goodnight, *boss.*"

"Wait. *What?*" He looks horrified.

"The water seemed pretty cold in the shower," I say.

This time when I turn my back on him, I make sure to add an extra swing to my hips before I enter my room and lock the door behind me.

I don't think Callahan Sharpe has ever had to work hard to get a woman. He said as much that first night.

If I'm worth it to him, then he'll figure it out.

And hearing him grit out a grated *Fuck* on the other side of the door is all the affirmation I need. I *never* would have stood up to Clint like I just did to Callahan. *I like this new, stronger me.*

I collapse on my bed with a victorious grin on my lips and anticipation humming through my blood.

CHAPTER THIRTEEN

Sutton

COFFEE.

That's my first thought when I stumble out of bed.

Callahan.

He's my second.

Last night was . . . frustrating, sexy, unexpected . . . empowering. Sure, I stuck to my word and held tight to it, but my dreams let me know exactly what I was missing by walking away. Boy, did they.

And now I must get coffee before I head out to the office they've assigned me and "officially" start my time here at Ocean's Edge.

The question is, what is the right answer?

What is it that Callahan can offer me that will be enough for me to risk everything I have going for me?

Or maybe it's more an exercise for him to think more of me than the one-night stand girl. We will be working with each other after all, and I need him to respect me and think of me as an equal. You can't exactly do that when the first time you meet, you drop your skirt without a second thought and then cave again soon after that.

I'm not an idiot in thinking our time spent will be anything more than *wild monkey sex* as Lizzy called it, but if he has to earn it, then maybe he'll be less likely to be careless about keeping what's happening a secret.

Because it does have to remain a secret or Roz would have me out on my ass in seconds for risking any future work with Sharpe International.

Roz.

Jesus.

She'd kill me for any and all of this. What happened to me? Why am I even risking this for sex?

I guess I'll have time to figure out the answer to that while he figures out his answer to me.

Besides, it might be fun in the meantime. A little flirting. A lot of wanting and not getting. Hell, we jumped right to the endgame. Maybe a little cat and mouse will be good for a bit.

Will wanting and not having be hard? Hell, yes.

But I also think it'll be worth it.

How will Callahan be toward me today after I threw him for a loop and literally left him hanging last night? I bet that's never happened before.

Even worse, how hard will it be for me to concentrate with him near?

I rub the sleep from my eyes as I shuffle out of the bedroom and then jolt to a stop when I hear the sound of a spoon stirring against the ceramic of a coffee cup.

And there, in the kitchen of my villa, is Callahan. With nothing on but a pair of workout shorts and running shoes. His hair is wet with waves of it going every which way, and the muscles in his back ripple as he doctors the cup of coffee in front of him.

"Um . . . What are you still doing here?"

Unfazed by the sound of my voice, Callahan watches the creamer as he pours it into his cup. "Making coffee. There's more than *enough* left in the pot if you want some," he says as casual as can be.

"That's not what I asked."

Callahan turns and looks at me for the first time. Jesus. *Seriously?* After a long, restless night of no sleep, thinking about him, this is how he greets me?

His cheeks are flushed from what I assume was a run or some other form of exercise. And that assumption is based off the V of sweat that darkens the front of his shorts. Said shorts that unknowingly might or might not currently be showcasing the ridge of the head of his cock.

"I'm sorry. I was distracted." He flashes a grin that tells me he knows exactly what distracted me and it was on purpose. "What did you ask, Sutton?"

"This is my room. Villa. Whatever you want to call it."

"That's not a question."

"Clearly."

"And your point is what?" He leans against the counter behind him and takes a sip of his coffee. He hisses from its heat, but his eyes stay locked on mine above the rim of the cup.

"That you're here. That you're making coffee as if—"

"As if I own the place?" The grin he flashes is mischievous as all hell. "Well . . ."

"That's not cool."

"I thought it was pretty witty," he says.

"No."

"Then charming at least."

I emit an exasperated sigh. First, I get domineering, sexy Callahan. Then I get brooding, I'm going to pretend I'm not Johnnie Walker, Callahan. And now I get playful, boyish Callahan. I don't want him to be any of them because it's damn attractive.

"Whether you own the place or not," I try again, "that doesn't give you the right to make yourself at home."

He points to the second room in the villa. "Considering that's my room, I'm supposed to be making myself at home."

"Come again?"

A smile ghosts over his lips. "That's the plan."

"Answer my question," I grit out, trying to ignore anything charming or seductive or sexy that he does or says.

"That's my room." A nonchalant shrug. "So that makes this our shared living space, and therefore I have every right to make myself at home, right?"

"No. It can't be."

"Pretty sure it is. Either that or someone's going to get pissed that my clothes are in his or her closet."

"No. Your stuff wasn't in there last night."

"You sure like that word a lot."

"What word?" I ask, his change of topic throwing me.

"No."

"No, I don't."

His grin widens. "You should learn to embrace the word yes more.

101

Supposedly giving in to the pleasures saying *yes* helps you live a longer, happier life."

"You think you're cute, don't you?"

"I know I am. Although I prefer words like sexy or handsome or devastating. I think those have more panache to them, don't you?"

I stare at him and his devilish grin and his incredibly absurd abs and know he's winning this round. Him and his ridiculous comments and sheepish smile.

"I think you need to explain why you're staying in my villa."

"The A/C in mine went out."

"Open a window," I say dryly.

"You were so preoccupied wanting me last night, that you assumed I was here for pleasure. Kind of like I was your *fuck toy*, although that term is offensive in so many ways, so let's not use it." He takes a sip of coffee, clearly pleased with the show he is putting on right now. "Oh, I forgot to ask you."

"Ask me what?"

"How your regret tastes this morning."

"My regret?" I laugh the word out. "What are you talking about?"

"The regret you felt after you walked away last night. The regret you felt as you lay in bed alone when I could have been occupying it with you." He licks his bottom lip. "Especially when you know how good *it* can be."

"*It?*"

"Yes. Sex." His eyes fire with suggestion. He sets his coffee cup down and crosses his arms over his chest. Of course, my eyes drift to his biceps when they flex with the motion, but then his words hit my ears. "*With me.*"

He walks over to the coffee pot and pours some into a new mug before reaching out with it to me. I stare at the cup, clearly a peace offering that I one hundred percent don't trust.

"It's just coffee," he says.

"It's just coffee from you, though."

He sets it on the counter beside me and then steps back, scrubbing a hand over his unshaven jaw. "Is this going to be a problem? Us working together when you want me so desperately?"

"I think you should ask yourself the same question." I step into him so that when I breathe in, the tight buds of my nipples rub against his chest. "We're going to be working beside each other, day in and day out, and now we're going to be sharing the same living space." I step back to allow enough space to trail my finger down the middle of his chest. His abs tense as he sucks in a breath. "Looks to me like you created the problem yourself, now didn't you, Callahan?"

"You've given me an impossible question to answer." He reaches out to grab my hip and I grab his wrist to stop him.

"Maybe you're not used to having to work for anything worthwhile," I murmur, our lips inches apart, our bodies physically vibrating with need and want. "Answer the question, and I'm yours."

He groans as he overpowers my hold on his wrist and puts his hand on my ass, pulling me against him so I can feel every long, hard inch of him.

"You don't want to play with this fire," he whispers, the warmth of his breath on my lips.

"*Maybe I look forward to being burned.*"

His eyes hold mine. "That's how you're going to play this, huh? Tease my cock, test my restraint, and then not let me have you."

"It's here. It's yours for the taking." We breathe in sync as my words take hold. His eyes darken, his body tenses. "The question remains though. What's in this for me?"

He takes my hand and places it over his cock I was just admiring through his shorts. "I think this is a pretty self-explanatory answer."

The ache between my thighs comes to life (as if it ever really stopped) and the suggestion in his gaze alone has me remembering to breathe.

I jolt back a step, needing space from the man who clouds my senses and thoughts. I grab the cup of coffee and move to the counter. I add too much creamer. Then sugar when I already added sugar. Anything to occupy my hands from reaching out and touching him.

"It's a dangerous game you're playing here, Collins," Callahan says with a tsk that is so dominant and sexy I can imagine him doing it in the bedroom.

"I have a feeling you're used to playing games."

I feel the warmth of his body behind me, smell the scent of his skin, and the heat of his breath on my shoulder as he dips his mouth to my ear. "I don't normally play games. I don't have to. I take what I want . . . but I'll play, this time. This once. I'll play because you might be the only bright spot for me in this fucking place. I know the prize and fuck if it's not worth waiting for." He slides a hand around my front and cups me. "But be warned, I'm not patient, especially when what I want is sexy as hell and within reach."

He licks a line down the curve of my neck before he steps back and walks out the villa's door.

CHAPTER FOURTEEN

Callahan

I'VE JUST FUCKED MYSELF, HAVEN'T I?

The question replays through my mind over and over as I walk across the property. It was even the cadence I repeated as I took my second run in as many hours.

But I had to get out of that villa. Away from Sutton and things I've never found sexy before—bedhead, pillow creases on cheeks, and husky morning voices—but now suddenly do after one fucking morning. Away from her flimsy sleep tank that you can see the pink of her nipples through and her question I don't have the fucking answer to.

Correction. I have the answer. Hot sex. Great sex. Endless sex.

That would be a good enough answer for almost any woman who's had the pleasure of experiencing it with me. Every woman, except for her.

I know why it bugs me, any man would, but what I can't put my finger on is why it's sexy as hell too.

Being denied.

Being challenged.

Having to work for something I've never had to work for before.

Hell, I walked into that suite that first night wanting nothing more than some good sex with the woman who intrigued and challenged me at Club Coquette. Now I've set it up so that I'm essentially living with her, seeing her, and being tempted by her every goddamn day.

Something is definitely wrong with me, because the answer to my own question is, yes, *I just fucked myself.*

There's no way to rationalize it. No way to make me feel less crazy because there's not an ounce of logic to it. I had her. I wanted her. I swore I wouldn't let myself have her. And now I'm determined to have her again.

There.

I said it. (*Again.*)

Now what to do about it.

Answering the fucking question would be the logical thing to do but what's the answer? I can't promise her the promotion with Roz because I have no control over that. I can't offer her a job at S.I.N. because then she'd be fucking her way to the top. I won't give her money and she said she didn't want that.

So what the hell does she want? What's her angle? The woman clearly still wants me as much as I want her. That want isn't in question. It's the why and the how and fuck if I know how to satisfy her to get it.

In any other situation I'd think I'm being played, but she's not playing me. She's dead fucking serious.

What do I get out of it?

I take another sip of my coffee and lift a hand in greeting to a staff member coming down the pathway across from me.

So yeah, I'll play this game of hers, but I'll add my terms too. After all, every great negotiation has to have two opponents. She's not the only one who can touch and entice and then withhold the endgame.

I'm already screwed as it is, so I might as well go all in. If I have to suffer, she has to suffer too.

"Morning," I say to no one in particular as I walk into the shared office space on the way to my own private one. I keep my eyes focused on my phone, pretending like I have a very important text I'm reading. I know Sutton is there, can smell her perfume and feel her eyes on me, but I don't look up or even acknowledge her.

If there's one thing I've found, it's that ignoring someone makes that person want you even more.

She wants to play? Let's play.

Greetings are muttered back as I take a seat at my desk. It takes a few seconds before chatter resumes, that cautious fear that the person in charge will get upset if people are talking wanes with each passing minute.

"So that's the plan?" Brady asks, his voice outside of my office.

"You say that like it's a bad plan," Sutton says.

"Not bad, no," he backpedals. "I'm just trying to figure out how you're going to complete that action list you have taped to the wall behind you that looks like it's a million miles long while going out and doing all of *these* things."

"These *things* are what's going to make Ocean's Edge stand out and be more attractive. I have to see what everyone else offers that we don't. Only then can we make ourselves better."

"And you plan on doing this in the two-month timeline you've given yourself to turn this beast around?" There is doubt laced in his voice, and I wish I could see Sutton's expression because I've no doubt she's shaking her head, already on the defensive.

"The financials won't be turned around in two months, Brady. You and I both know that. But there will be a plan in place for you to build on a stronger foundation by then. The staff should be happier with the new pay structure we're going to offer, the amenities will be more competitive with other resorts, a change in design esthetic will be underway, and a bolder, more attractive marketing plan will be in motion." There is a pause as if she's doing something, and then she continues. "Almost all of those things can be done from right here in my chair, but not the amenities part. That part I need to experience, so I can compare with what we have."

"I wasn't questioning you," Brady murmurs.

"I know you weren't," Sutton says, and I can hear the reassuring smile in her tone. "I'm fine with being challenged and questioned. That will only serve to make this revamp more successful. Don't ever worry about that."

She's good with people. She can read the room and tell Brady is worried he's stepped on her toes. It's something not everyone can do.

Brady moves around his desk, out of my sight, and I presume over to hers. "Are you going off that website?"

"No. I've cross-checked about ten 'best-of' lists and have curated the ones that are duplicated the most. I figure that will give me the best feel of what people are wanting when they visit the island."

"Smart."

"Here's the list I've made so far."

Brady makes an approving hum. "These are ones I would have picked as well. Why is that one highlighted?"

"Because that, my friend, requires tickets and I plan on making sure I have one."

"To One-Night-Stand Land?"

And before the last word is out of Brady's mouth, I am up and out of my seat, casually strolling into their office with my hands in my pockets to prevent them from fisting.

"What was that?" I ask.

"Sutton here is going to be the guinea pig and try out all of the 'best ofs' for the island so we can make ours better. Including, singles night at Isla del Mar.

Singles night?

"Oh. I thought I heard something different," I murmur.

"You did," Sutton says more than enthusiastically. I turn to look at her, take in her tumble of hair falling over her shoulders and dark pink shirt, but it's the smile on her face and look in her eyes that grabs my attention. Mocking. Amused. "Brady called it One-Night-Stand Land. That's what it's often referred to in some of the reviews."

I purse my lips and nod. "I thought it was understood that we're trying to target a higher-end clientele. *One-Night-Stand Land* doesn't exactly denote class, Sutton."

Her back straightens. Yes, I just insulted both of us if for no other purpose than to get her attention.

And it worked.

Her eyes fire with anger.

"I'm well aware of the market we're catering to in the property's makeover. But that market—the single, rich kids who take their private jets down here to throw away Daddy's money on the Instagram vacations, frequent that place in droves."

"Your point?" I ask.

"My point is we have a club on the premises that hasn't been anywhere near fifty percent capacity since the club at Isla del Mar started doing singles night last year. And what I learned from talking to the manager this morning is that those socialites ready to spend Daddy's money go there because there is nowhere else for them to go on the island. My bet is those clients want upscale. They want to go where they can get bottle service and velvet ropes of a VIP section like they get back home. They want to be treated like royalty so they can have fun while not having to mix with the little people."

"This is the Caribbean, not Manhattan."

"They want what they want and will go to the places that provide it." She leans back in her chair and crosses her arms over her chest.

"And?" I ask.

"And we have a club that can provide that for them. We fancy it up. We make capacity limited for non-resort guests, maybe a lottery you have to apply for—something like that—because clearly whatever is off-limits makes people want it more, wouldn't you agree?" she asks, lifting a lone eyebrow to drive that point home.

"For some, yes." I lean against the doorjamb, knowing she has a damn good point.

"Sometimes the allure of something is more potent than actually having it," she says.

"And other times it's not worth the hassle," I say, slowly turning to meet her eyes. There's a defiant lift to her chin and a smirk on that fuckable mouth of hers.

"It works. I've seen it happen before at another resort I consulted on."

"So that's your plan? Tease them with the allure?"

"Yes." Her smile grows. "And ultimately asking myself if what we offer them at Ocean's Edge is enough. *What's in it for them?* What are they getting out of these different attractions and excursions that seal the deal?"

I have to tell myself to look away. To not challenge that stare and those words of hers or Brady and everyone else in here will know exactly what I want to do. Fuck that mouth and those lips that keep up their sassy teasing.

But I stay put and meet her eyes. "*What's in it for them?*"

"Yes." The word is slow and deliberate as she fights a smile.

"A good time. Memories. Stepping outside of their box. *Feeling alive.*" I lift a brow. "I'd say those are all things that come with the territory that most anyone would be content with."

"Some people want to be more than content."

Silence falls for a beat. I want to kiss that smirk off her lips, but thankfully Brady takes the opportunity to break the spell.

"I know I'm not the brightest bulb in the room, but I'm lost. Are we still talking about Isla del Mar and One-Night-Stand Land or did we move on and I missed it?"

I turn on my heel and walk to the window, hands shoved in my pockets. It's easier to study the couple walking toward the beach than turn and face the two of them.

Fucking Sutton.

"We're still on the club, Brady. No worries. Sutton has a way of talking in metaphors at times that make no sense to us men." I turn back to face them and flash a smug smile. "And since you already know this whole scenario in upgrading our club works, then there's no need for you to go there and subject yourself to cheesy pickup lines and slobbering drunks. I'm more than certain your time would be better spent with you and Brady working over numbers at projections on making this work."

I look from her to Brady and give a curt nod before retreating back into my office.

The land of one-night stands, my ass.

Like I'm going to let her hang out there by herself where other men can look and want and touch when I can't.

It takes a few seconds for my . . . what—*anger, frustration, disbelief?* —to abate before the numbers on my laptop in front of me make sense.

Numbers. This was the part my dad loved, and I hated. We'd butt heads. He liked to work from start to finish. I preferred to take the end result and massage it backwards. It always caused a fight. It always ended up with me storming out while Ledger and Ford sat there and appeased him by doing it his way.

I'd get a call a few hours later. A short lecture about how the wheel doesn't need to be reinvented all at once and a request to not fight the system next time. Then there would be a non-apology, apology in true Maxton Sharpe fashion, and an offer to meet up at the golf course later.

Leaning back, I smile at the memory. Even after these past months, it still hurts to know those calls aren't coming, that the dynamic between us that only we had, will never be again. But the smiles come a bit easier now, the memories not so hard to think about.

I know my brothers share in the grief, but they also share in a resentment I understood but could never stop. What our father did wasn't right—even I know that—but there was no changing Maxton Sharpe's ways, good, bad, or otherwise. My only hope is that with time, they'll learn to understand that maybe it's what he needed.

And I was simply trying to make him happy.

CHAPTER FIFTEEN

Callahan

Ten Years Ago

"WAIT A MINUTE. YOU'RE SAYING THIS IS OUR FAULT?" Ledger says, exasperated and frustrated as all three of us stand before our father.

No one refuses a summons from Maxton Sharpe.

But I sure as hell wanted to.

Especially now.

"I'm saying he's your little brother and it's Ford's and your responsibility to look out for each other," our father says.

"Little brother by five minutes, Dad," Ledger says.

"Exactly. We're all the same age," Ford says and then looks at me. "I love you, man, but your bullshit is your bullshit and I'm over it. I refuse to let it drag me down too."

I nod. It's all I can do because my focus is on after this meeting. On the wrath I'm more than certain my dad is going to lay upon me—or threaten me with—that will be way worse than my brothers' dismay.

"You're family. The three of you will be all you'll have someday," my father says. "So yes, it is your responsibility to pick each other up and carry each other when the other falls."

"You're right," Ford defends, "we are family. And sometimes when family fails because they are too busy with their head up their ass partying and getting laid, you let them fail and learn the hard way instead of enabling them by babying them."

"Dad, in their defense," I interrupt, even though it's probably best for my own sake to keep my mouth shut— "it's not right to blame them for—"

"See?" our father says, pointing at me. "That's exactly what you two should be doing. Defending him like he's defending you right now. That's what family does."

"With all respect, sir," Ledger says, the derision in his voice not masked particularly well. "Where was this lecture when I was failing undergrad? I believe the words you told me were *don't be an embarrassment to the Sharpe name. That if I couldn't figure my shit out, I might as well get a new last name.*" His eyes harden. "I'm not hearing any of that right now."

"I love you and treat you all the same," he says and not one of us believes it. Not even him.

"No, you don't," Ledger says angrily. "If this were Ford or me dropping out of Wharton, you'd have kicked our asses out and threatened our inheritance. We would have heard the endless *no one embarrasses Maxton Sharpe* bullshit. But it's not us. It's Callahan and he can never do any wrong in your eyes."

I stand there more than ashamed and hating that with each passing second, the weight on my shoulders that had lifted by finally dropping out of Wharton, is being piled back on with every one of Ledger's and Ford's words.

Our father's sigh is heavy. "I expect to see your up-to-date grades on my desk by tomorrow morning."

"You mean Ledger's and my grades, right?" Ford asks. "What is it that you're requiring from Callahan to keep his place and prestige in this family and company?"

"I think I can handle my own son," he says, making it clear the conversation is over. He lifts his eyebrows, welcoming the challenge, but neither Ledger nor Ford do. They're well versed in this, and I fucking hate that I'm in the middle of it. "You're dismissed."

All three of us visibly release a sigh of relief.

"Callahan, sit down."

Fuck.

I guess it's deserved though considering I am the one who dropped out of one of the best business schools in the country. One my brothers— my equals—are kicking ass at.

The weight of his stare is unnerving as he waits for the room to clear. The door clicks. The dread hits.

"Explain yourself." Two words and fucking endless possibilities.

"I can't learn like that, Dad. If I read one more textbook or create one more spreadsheet, I'm going to stab my eyes out."

"That's a bit dramatic, son."

"I'm hands on, Dad. I always have been. School is a lesson in futility, and in learning that if you stroke a professor's ego long enough by filling his head with how great he is, you'll ace the course. Why am I forced to regurgitate facts and statistics when I can be out in the world creating my own?"

"You need the foundation though. You need the structure and the—"

"Fuck the structure," I say and then wince, waiting for the reprimand, but when I look at him, I'm shocked to see a soft smile on his lips and affection in his eyes.

"*You're just like her.*"

I don't ask who he's talking about because I already know. *Mom.*

"She was spontaneous and hated convention and bucked the system more times than not. She was . . ."

I've heard it all before but let him talk anyway. I know the words he's going to say and the adjectives he's going to describe her with, just as I know how his eyes are going to fill with tears he only ever cries for her.

He may have had many girlfriends since her death, but our mom was the true love of his life. I truly think he never got over her death and so sometimes he looks to me to remember her.

She was his soft spot.

As I am now.

"I'd tell you dropping out is unacceptable, Callahan, but I know it doesn't matter to you. You simply don't care about my opinions or that you've given new meaning to the Sharpe legacy at Wharton. *And not in a good way.*" He sighs heavily as he leans back in his chair and levels a stare at me. "I sat and questioned how I was going to handle this, handle you. I wondered what kind of lesson I'd be teaching you by allowing this sort of thing to happen. What do you have to say for yourself?"

I stare at my father. He's tough as nails expecting the most out of his boys. His name and his legacy mean everything to him, so to have one of us fail was never an option.

But Ledger is right. When he struggled with the everyday expectations of duty as a Sharpe and college course load, my dad had no mercy or sympathy for him. He held him to the fire with words about being a disappointment and threats about losing his place in the Sharpe dynasty.

Ford and I worried about him. His mental health. His state of mind. But that toughness is what spurred him to shake out of his funk and currently be sitting at the top of our class. Failure isn't an option.

Is it because Ledger is a cookie cutter of our father that Dad accepted no less?

And does the same hold true to me? Because I'm our mother that I get more leeway than a child should get?

What about Ford? Is he a mixture of both so our father is hard in some ways and not in others, so he's left in that middle child, no-man's land where he wonders where he falls?

He loves us all. No doubt there. But he loves us in a way so very different that at times it's unfair.

The issue? Just like now, I'm too fucking grateful not to be held to a bar of their height that I just shut my mouth and smile.

"Well?" he asks.

I rub my hands on my thighs and think of the shit I've done, the stunts I've pulled. "There's nothing to say that I haven't already said. I'm not going to apologize for being who I am, Dad. I'm not going to kiss your ass and beg you to forgive me for disappointing you. I am who I am. A Sharpe who doesn't live up to your standards. I live up to mine, and right or wrong, that's me."

He twists his lips and swivels back and forth in his chair. "And your plans moving forward?"

"I don't know." I have no problem whatsoever with hard work, but sitting in an office with a tie cinched around my neck every day isn't exactly what does it for me.

"You will not rest on your laurels."

"No one said I was going to."

A smile ghosts his lips. "You're your mother, remember? I do know you."

He rises from his seat and moves to his favorite corner of his office, shoves his hands in his pockets, and stares at the people down below. It's his thinking corner. The place where he makes decisions.

I know better than to speak, than to push him to decide when I want out of this recirculated air and concrete confinement.

"Then you start your tenure with Sharpe International Network today."

Oh Jesus.

Dropping out of school meant I was going to get fresh air and freedom. It meant I was going to be able to sit back and decide who I was without being surrounded by people who only looked at me as a Sharpe. *Who only want to know me because of my last name.*

I close my eyes and quietly groan.

This would be my brothers' dream. To jump onto the pedestal and start their climb up the corporate ladder. The ladder that is superficial since they'd be walking in day one on the top rung. This is their everything.

And they'll see it as more favoritism. More *Callahan is the pet.*

To me, I was just handed a death sentence.

CHAPTER SIXTEEN

Sutton

"I FEEL LIKE I JUST GOT YOU BACK AND NOW I'VE LOST YOU AGAIN," Lizzy says through the phone.

"But you've lost me for good reasons this time." I lean back on the lounger and soak up the afternoon sun.

"True. True. But I still miss you nonetheless."

"It feels good to be missed."

"Speaking of missing you . . ." she says with some hesitation. "I got a call last night from Clint."

"Clint?"

"Mm-hmm. You missed a dinner with his boss or something and since you weren't answering your phone, he called me."

"I'm sorry." I scrunch my nose and think of the numerous all-caps messages I received from him last night. The threats and belittlements and then the apologies and the acting like the first texts were never sent. What amazes me is how I responded though. It's more than clear that Clint is emotionally abusive. I'm sad I stayed as long as I did. But leaving was the absolute best move I could have made. Time and distance have allowed me to see this. To acknowledge this. "I didn't want to answer him. He never should have called you."

"I'll take the calls and the opportunity to let him know what a dick he is any day of the week. You keep on not picking up the phone and having fun there."

"Thanks. I truly didn't mean—"

"End of story, Sutt. Don't apologize. Now . . . on to that man of yours. Tell me all the details."

"There's not much to tell."

"You're living with him. That means there is a whole lot to tell."

"There may have been some flirting and some heavy petting—"

"Keep going . . ."

"But I needed to draw the line somewhere. He's who he is and I'm who I am."

"Meaning you have the most to lose."

"Exactly." I think of my status update meeting with Roz earlier and her palpable excitement over this project. "So I gave him an ultimatum that sounded great but now that the moment has passed, it feels like such an immature thing to do."

"You were, *are*, protecting yourself. What was the question?"

"What's in it for me?" I feel stupid even saying it now.

"Exceptional and long-lasting dick, obviously."

"Lizzy." I sigh her name out.

"Well? It's true." She laughs. "What else can he say? Money? A raise?"

"I told him those weren't the answers."

"You do like him though, right? Because those are the only answers he can give." She snorts. "It was ridiculous, but I kind of love it."

"Why?"

"Because it'll make the man get creative. And if a guy like that, who can have anyone, actually tries to answer you, then you at least know he's really interested."

"I guess." I start to say something and then stop.

"Spill it, Sutt."

"Do you know how hard it is to work with someone, see their aloofness and authority, knowing what he sounds like when he orders you to spread your legs?" I swear I blush a thousand shades of red.

"Girl, please tell me you sit in meetings and fantasize about him bending you over that desk and having his way with you."

Wasn't I doing just that this afternoon? Having a whole, full-blown fantasy while we were reviewing staff numbers and salary efficiency?

"Perhaps," I finally answer.

Her laugh is the only sound I need to hear. She knows she's right.

CHAPTER SEVENTEEN

Callahan

THERE'S SOMETHING ABOUT DAY DRINKING THAT MAKES everything better.

And there's definitely something about having a beer or two while on the clock that feels like a quiet *fuck you* to my brothers for the ultimatum they gave me before I left. The one that keeps eating at me when I have two seconds to think straight outside of this massive influx of information I'm trying to process.

Talk about drinking water through a firehose.

Besides, it's been two weeks of nose to the grindstone, and it's high time I made friends with the head bartender at the resort. I've always found bartenders have a finger on the pulse of the guests and the management they work for.

Keone didn't disappoint with his inside information on the other resorts that are slowly wheedling our staff away. At the complaints he hears the guests grumble. And at what he sees from where he stands as an observer and a listener.

Besides, I found it much easier unwinding by chatting with a three-hundred-pound Samoan gentle giant than fighting the good fight against Sutton. Because I'm tired, I have a headache, I'm horny, and I'm more than sexually frustrated.

What's in it for me is a whole lot of nothing, if I'm honest.

"She wants you, you know."

"Excuse me?" I ask Keone.

"The lady at the end of the bar. She's eyeing you like she wants you for dessert," he says, his accent subtle as he keeps his head down while running a towel over the counter beside me when it's not even dirty.

I know who he's referring to. I've caught her looking a few times since I've been here. She's pretty in a mom way. No doubt she has two kids back in the room who are constantly fighting, is tired from taking care of everyone, and just wants thirty minutes of fun.

Definitely not my scene, but I still feel for her needing a break.

"Yeah. I saw her," I murmur before taking another sip of beer.

"Wouldn't be a good wingman if I didn't tell you." His laugh thunders around the patio, and I dare anyone not to smile at the sound of it.

He takes care of a few more customers as I watch the ebb and flow of foot traffic. Most people are heading to the beach. Some are heading to the pool. Others look like they definitely forgot to put sunscreen on and need to stay out of this strong Caribbean sun.

My mind drifts to Sutton and her bullshit one-night stand ploy in the office earlier this week.

Was that supposed to make me jealous? Make me fight harder and want her more?

I want her all right. That's never been in question.

Was it supposed to make me figure out the answer to her fruitless fucking question that the more I think about has no real answer to?

Fuck.

"What's got you so serious, man?" Keone asks on the next pass around.

"Tell me something. When a woman asks *what's in it for me*, what the fuck is she actually saying?"

Another roar of his laugh. "You got women problems? Jesus, that doesn't bode well for me with you looking like you do and me looking like I do." He rubs his round belly and flexes.

"Not women problems. Just . . ."

What the fuck are you doing, Cal? Asking advice from the bartender about a woman you just met because you need to find an answer to an impossible question so you can get laid?

Let's add rambling thoughts like an idiot to the list while I'm at it.

"Just . . ." Keone leans an elbow on the bar and asks.

"It's nothing."

"That's bullshit, but I respect a man keeping his business, his business."

He takes a sip of water and wipes the beads of sweat off his head with a handkerchief he pulls from his back pocket. "But I tell you this, Boss Man, women like three things. To laugh, to feel wanted, and little gestures."

"Little gestures?"

"Yes, man. It lets them know you care and—"

"It's not like that," I say. "It's—she's—"

"Ahhh," he says, drawing the sound out. "I hear you. I feel you, brother. She's not putting her clothes in your drawers anytime soon." He fist-bumps me. "Nothing wrong with that now, is there?"

I chuckle and down the rest of my beer instead of responding.

"You in the game playing phase. You chase or she chase?" he asks and slides another beer in front of me without asking.

"That's the question of the day, isn't it?"

CHAPTER EIGHTEEN

Callahan

WHEN I LEAVE THE BAR AN HOUR LATER WITH instructions to put the lady at the end of the bar's drinks on my tab, I feel slightly more relaxed.

The sun is still out for a few hours yet since it sets later here than I'm used to, and the facts and figures that have loaded down my mind are swimming somewhere beneath the haze of beer running through my blood.

I stop in front of the villa and stare at the door. Our first night here, I was quite sure I was winning at life when I made sure the two of us were rooming together, and now it just feels like I'm standing with my dick in my hand and fucking losing.

To have her within reach and want her desperately but to not be able to have her because of some bullshit, unanswerable question.

Fuck that.

I'm Callahan Sharpe. Any woman would kill to be with me. It's time she knows that.

I march to the door and yank it open with a purpose, dead set on getting what I want. On getting her.

"Sutton." It's a command. Plain and simple.

"*Callahan?* Is something wrong?" Sutton walks out of her bedroom, fastening an earring through her ear. "Are you okay?"

She stops mid stride when she sees me, and I'm sure the concerned look on her face is because my jaw is probably dragging on the floor.

Standing in the middle of the villa is Sutton in a bright red bikini that highlights and emphasizes every glorious goddamn inch of her. Legs and abs and tits and . . . *Christ.*

Staring at her, I feel like a man drowning for water, and she *is* the water.

I clear my throat. "Yeah. I'm fine."

"Did you need something?"

"No—I don't think—"

"Ooops," she says as her earring falls to the ground. I hiss out a breath when she bends over to pick it up and gives me a full showing of the teeny, tiny bottoms that go between her perfectly round ass.

"Are you going somewhere?" I take a step forward, not hiding the fact that I'm enjoying the view.

"Yes. Out. To the beach."

"*In that?*"

Sutton looks at her body and then at her ass before looking up at me with a blank stare on her face. "It is a bathing suit. You wear it to the beach. So yeah, *in this.*"

"You can't wear that." *Smooth. Real smooth, Sharpe.*

"Excuse me?" She laughs the words out.

"It's too small and it shows way too much." I walk to the fridge and grab another beer. I sound like a dick but don't care as I fumble for a reason other than no one else deserves to see this, to see her like this, than me. "It's not an appropriate choice of attire when staff can see you."

"Good thing I'm going offsite to a beach on a non-Sharpe property then." She smiles sarcastically. "You sure you need another one of those? You seem a little keyed up."

"I need one." *Fucking hell do I need one if she's going out in that.*

"Okay." She draws the word out and takes a few steps toward me.

Wrong move on her part.

I smell the scent of her sunscreen now. Can see the dusting of freckles over her chest. Can see how easy it would be to pull the strings on those bottoms and have her undressed in a heartbeat.

"Is there something that's bugging you, Callahan?"

"You."

"Me?" She chuckles, angling her head to the side and staring at me. "What did I do?"

"You're driving me fucking crazy," I say and take a step toward her. For some reason I expect her with her silly game to back away, but she doesn't. She stands her ground.

"Good."

"Not good." I take another step. "Women don't say no to me. Did you know that?" I cup the side of her face. Her breath hitches. *She wants me.* She so fucking wants me, and the sight of it is like a goddamn high. "They want me. They chase me." I lean in so my lips hover over hers. "I never chase, Collins."

"And I've never had a one-night stand before." She inhales a shaky breath. "So there. We're even."

My chuckle is low and even and desperate sounding. "We're far from even. I want you." I lean in and go to press a kiss to her lips but she moves her head to the side. I take what I can get and lace a row of open-mouthed kisses down the line of her jaw. Jesus Christ. Her taste. Her soft moan. The sudden goosebumps chasing over her skin. The feel of her body yielding to mine.

She definitely wants me.

The beer has nothing on what Sutton Pierce does to me.

"And you're still my boss," she murmurs on a sigh.

"Collins. Please." I lick a line over her shoulder. She tastes like salt and sex. My hands fist into balls because I'm desperate to touch and take, and I know if I start, I won't be able to stop myself until I have every fucking inch of her.

"I can't. We can't. I'm not making you chase," she murmurs. "I promise. I'm simply making you appreciate the prize."

"Fuck me, Sutton. Right here. Right now. Take me."

Her laugh is low and throaty as she scratches her nails down the front of my shirt, my dick jumping to attention at the sensation. "Seems someone is taking their own advice about begging."

The knock on the door is loud, but it takes a second to seep into my subconscious and react. But by the time I do, Sutton has already jumped back a few feet and is smirking at me. "Saved by the bell."

I step forward, put my hand against the small of her back, and yank her against me. "I promise you nothing's going to save you from me." My chuckle is smothered when I don't give her time to react or back away and brand my lips to hers. The kiss is angry and hungry and fueled with a desperation I've never felt before for someone.

It's because I can't have her. I know it. She knows it. Or maybe it's because I know I can have it, but I'm too fucking fixated on her that I can't figure out the answer.

"Sutton? You there?" There is more knocking on the front door.

"Callahan." She presses her hands against my chest, but I steal one more kiss. "I have to get the door."

She goes to walk away, but her hand is in mine and I hold her still. "You kissed me. You can deny that you want this, but your touch says differently."

"I haven't denied anything." Her eyes flicker to my cock pressing against the seam of my pants. "The kiss. It was a minor transgression." She smirks. "My company is waiting for me."

She slips her hand out of mine and heads toward the front door, giving me a more than perfect view of how exactly small that itty-bitty bikini is.

Oh. Shit.

She was serious about going out like that. *In that.*

"Wait. Where are you going again?" I call after her.

"Look at you. *Damn.*"

Brady. *Jesus Christ.* It's the whole fucking family in one place. Great. I groan and lean against the counter as I down the rest of my beer, needing to hide my softening hard-on.

Wait. She's going with Brady in that bikini? Over my dead fucking body.

"Mr. Sharpe." I look up to see Brady standing there. The man is smart, and I'm sure he is more than assessing the situation and reading into it.

"Brady. Long time no see," I joke as he eyes me. My first thought is to address the hunch I see fleeting through his eyes but if I do, it'll just confirm it. Plus, he's in my employ so I don't owe him any fucking explanations. In a situation like this, nothing is better than something. "Have plans with Sutton?"

"We do. Yes." He looks around the villa, which I'm more than certain probably looks a lot like the one he lives in as lodging is part of his compensation package. "You know that we have much better accommodations for you than the staff quarters, right? The A/C parts are on the way for the villa you were booked in, but we can definitely put you in one of the guest suites or—"

"Thank you, but it's not necessary. That was the plan, but I'm settled here now. Besides, it's important to be in the same shoes as the staff so I can better understand how to improve their accommodations if need be."

Sutton rolls her eyes over his shoulders but thankfully chimes in to try and settle the definite curiosity that Brady has. "It's fine," she says with a nonchalant shrug. "It's not like I'm particularly thrilled with the idea either."

"Jesus," Brady barks out through a cough, his eyes wide with surprise that she just spoke of her boss that way. *With me present.*

Sutton looks over to me with an impish grin and a crinkle of her nose in a non-apology before looking back at Brady. "Hate to break it to you, Sharpe, but no one is supposed to like their boss."

I struggle with a witty comeback because the things I want to say can't exactly be stated in front of Brady without proving her point—that I can't be discreet. My mouth is open, the words are fumbling around in my head, when she steps in and takes the reins.

"The plus side? We're rarely here together and when we are, Callahan's a morning person and I'm a night owl. So it works out just fine. Besides, it's a good thing he didn't take the Luxe Suite since it just booked last night for a five-week extended stay."

"I heard," Brady says, the topic and awkwardness suddenly gone. "No complaints here. I'll have to introduce you to the guest when he arrives. He's a regular who has business on the islands. A Wall Street money man who definitely treats us well when he stays with us."

"Good. Great. I'd like that," Sutton says. "Let me grab my stuff, and I'll meet you outside."

"Yes. Okay." Brady shifts on his feet, uncomfortable. Clearly, he's intimidated by me. Good. Let's keep it that way. "I'll just wait outside then."

"Great." I nod and wait for the door to shut before walking into Sutton's room unannounced.

She startles. "Can I help you?"

"You're not wearing that." I point at her bikini.

"Thanks for your opinion, but I am." She glances in the mirror. "I like how it makes my ass look, don't you?"

Now she's just being a tease.

And it's working.

She takes her time wrapping a see-through sarong around her waist that does little to hide anything. "Better?"

"Hardly," I grunt, my buzz now completely gone. "Where are you going?"

"To item number nine on my list. Dinner at Crystal Beach. It's supposed to be a hot spot. I want to check it out and see how we can adapt something we have here to compete with it."

I don't care about dinner or beaches or anything. I care that other men are going to see her in that and want her like I do. I care about Brady getting the wrong idea and making a move on her because then I'd have to kill him. That would only serve to make matters worse considering his untimely death would leave me without a competent manager.

"And you think it's appropriate for your manager to see you in that?"

"It's covering where it needs to cover. Besides, I assure you that Brady and his husband don't care one bit about staring at my ass or my tits, but that's not your concern," she says as she walks past me toward the door.

"Brady's husband?"

"Yes. Husband." She turns around and looks at me over her shoulder. "Maybe if you stopped being an aloof asshole when you walk into the office and actually talked to your staff, you'd get a better feel for who you're working with."

"I don't fraternize with employees. It makes them think of you differently and lose respect for you. Number one rule in business."

"What a pity. You're missing out on a lot of great people." She purses her lips for a beat. "I guess that means you shouldn't fraternize with me either, then."

And with that, she sashays out of the villa, her hips swinging. I swear to God I can picture the smile on those pretty lips of hers. *She knows she won this round.*

CHAPTER NINETEEN

Sutton

I LET THE SHOWER'S WARM WATER SLUICE OVER MY BODY AND WAKE me up.

We had fun last night at the beach. It was nothing spectacular if I'm looking at it from a business perspective. But bonfires, locals playing classic favorites on guitars, and different food and cocktail stations gave it a kicked-back, fun atmosphere. Definitely low-key but with a high-class feel.

And then there were questions from Brady. His way of feeling out the situation between Callahan and me without asking point-blank. I think I evaded well enough, but will definitely have to make a point of being out of the villa as much as possible so I can avoid any further speculation. It was stupid of me not to think about it. Here I am worrying about the consequences of us sleeping together while not considering that people might assume it anyway since we're sharing the same villa.

That just goes to show how much Callahan clouds my thoughts and judgment. What if Roz hears we're sharing the same villa and assumes I'm sleeping with Callahan though? I have a feeling she'll be a lot harder to convince otherwise.

Why does this feel like déjà vu? A man controlling the narrative—my narrative—again, when I told myself, *never again.*

Hence, the question. *What's in it for me?* Those five words have given me back as much control as I can have in this situation without jeopardizing this opportunity. It's also made Callahan realize the uninhibited woman I was that first night is just a small part of the woman he has to work side by side with now.

And since I can't move villas, as I was told there is no other staff villa available for the moment, the only solution I've come up with is that I be here as little as possible when Callahan is. Maybe that will cut down on the possibility of rumors.

With a groan, I turn the shower off and force myself to think about options for Ocean's Edge and not Callahan. Do I suggest a rotating schedule of events that repeat every other week? That's typically long enough in between for the guests to turnover so they don't see a repeat night.

It's definitely an option.

More structure for the staff so they know what to expect. More options for the guests to enhance their stay.

Callahan will say that's what resorts that cater to the middle class do. I'll have to have facts and figures ready to suggest otherwise.

Callahan.

I grab the towel as thoughts of him fill my head. His drunken cuteness last night. How appalled he was at my bikini. The sputtering. The commands. The wide eyes.

Before he walked in, I wasn't one hundred percent certain I was going to keep the bikini on. I am here for work after all and was going out with Brady and his husband, so I figured it might not be appropriate. But the minute Callahan saw me and had objections to me wearing it, it cemented that I would most definitely be keeping it on.

He doesn't know that the moment I walked out the door, I pulled a sundress out of my bag and slipped it over the bikini. It was fun to bait him, though. To watch him lose control when he's a control freak.

But the man sure knows how to make his kiss leave a lasting impression on a woman.

It's hard to stick to your guns when you want him just as badly. It's even harder to not give in when he presses you against countertops and kisses you until your knees give out.

I check the clock to see how much time I have before my first meeting and then start pulling my clothes out to get dressed. It's when I get to my underwear drawer that I find it completely empty.

"What the hell?" I mutter and turn to look around my room as if my pairs of panties miraculously grew legs and walked out of the drawer.

I immediately start going through the rest of my dresser only to find my bathing suit bottoms are gone too.

My first thought is that some creep robbed us. I know it sounds weird, but I've been in a lot of hotels with my job and have heard a lot of stories.

With my towel wrapped around me, I throw open my door and stumble over a large box wrapped with a huge red bow at my feet.

What is going on here?

First my panties and now this?

I pick it up and set it on my bed, curious and confused when I see a card that has my name on it.

These should fix the problem.

—Johnnie

What?

When I lift the tissue-wrapped contents out of the box and open them, all I can do is laugh. There on my bed are the biggest, ugliest, granny panties in every boring color imaginable. We're talking full coverage fabric from below your ass cheeks to above your belly button granny panties. And at the very bottom of the pile are the most basic, black bathing suit bottoms that are much the same style.

My smile is wide as I shake my head at the contents in disbelief.

He really just did that.

I clutch my towel around me and grab my phone off the nightstand. He answers on the first ring.

"Sharpe," he says nonchalantly when he knows damn well who is calling him.

"You're kidding me, right?"

"About?" I can hear the smile in his tone.

"Granny panties? Seriously?"

I hear a door close, and I can assume he's shutting the door to his office for privacy from the rest of the staff. "Well, since I'm holding the rest of your panties and bikini bottoms hostage, I think you'll be happy with the many choices I provided you with."

"Are you insane?"

"Probably." He laughs, and I love that little sound of disbelief over the fact that he actually did this. Because that's exactly how I feel about the whole situation between the two of us.

"You went through my drawers?" I know I should be freaked by this. I'm not.

"You left your door and your drawer open when you walked out to leave me while playing with the staff. Curiosity got the best of me. I mean ... I was a *desperate* man. How could I not be when all of your underwear is completely sexy and more than a man in my dire situation needs to see or imagine." He coughs over a laugh.

"But you can imagine me wearing these?"

"It's so much easier on certain parts of my anatomy to imagine you in those, yes. So I took matters into my own hands."

"Clearly." I laugh. How can I not? "And now you're holding mine hostage?"

"I figured a certain ransom could be paid in order to hand them over, yes."

He's clever. I have to admit that. He's definitely clever.

"Tell me something. We're on an island in the middle of nowhere," I say.

"Yes, I'm aware."

"And you were able to get all of these at the drop of a dime?"

He chuckles. "It's amazing the things you can get when you have money."

"You're arrogant."

"I know. You love it."

I pick up a beige pair and hold them up. They're massive and like something my great grandma used to wear over her Depends when I was a kid.

"Full coverage," he says, interrupting my thoughts.

"What?"

"That's *what's in it for you.* Having your ass covered should someone find out about us."

My jaw falls lax and then I laugh. That was witty and clever and fitting. *I hate that I kind of love it.*

"Noted."

"But that's not the answer, is it?" he asks.

"Nope, but it was a pretty damn good take on it."

"I should get some kind of brownie points for that, don't you think?"

"Perhaps."

"Perhaps?" he asks. "About that ransom, then . . ."

"Nope. I'm good."

"What do you mean *you're good?*"

"Exactly like it sounds." I laugh. "I'm good."

"What happened to good, old-fashioned negotiations, huh?"

"Sometimes you just have to take matters into your own hands. You'd know all about that with those long, cold showers you seem to be taking. Goodbye, Callahan."

And then I hang up the phone without saying another word, needing to leave him hanging while I quietly swoon inside.

I chew on the inside of my cheek, my smile so wide my cheeks hurt. A flirting, creative Callahan is drop-your-panties hot.

Then again, I guess he already proved that in his own, unique way.

Game on, Sharpe.

CHAPTER TWENTY

Sutton

"WE'RE NOT A CRUISE SHIP, SUTTON," CALLAHAN SAYS from where he's leaning back in his chair, elbows on the arms, fingers steepled.

"I'm more than aware of that, but in my professional opinion, many of these amenities and experiences provide an added value to Ocean's Edge as a whole. While they may not appear to be 'high-end,' they do provide something your guests are seeking and will continue to seek regardless of their income."

"Continue." He holds his hands up as if he's expecting more from me.

"Brady and I have begun working on a comprehensive plan detailing each idea we'd like to begin implementing with the kind of minute details that I'm more than certain will make your eyes roll back in your head."

"Is that so?" He gives a ghost of a lopsided smirk, and I'm sure the suggestive look in his eyes implies my words—*eyes roll back in your head*—are making him think of other activities that can cause that.

"Yes. That is so." I clear my throat and don't back down from his stare, trying to remain professional in this space when people are milling about in the office just beyond, trying to waste away the remaining minutes of their workday. "Benchmarking reports against comparable resorts on the island. Looking at book patterns, the costs to implement these new options and ideas, their costs versus the return we'd receive and—"

"Yes. You're right. I'm already bored." His sigh is heavy. "Give me an example of one of these ideas."

"Ecotourism."

"Ecotourism?" His tone tells me he's already dismissed it.

"Yes. It's all the rage. Since the elite love to champion their causes—or at least look like they are while posting pics on social media and hashtagging up a storm—it's a necessary addition to keep the property in tune with one of the fastest growing travel trends."

"I assure you, I've never *hashtagged up a storm* for the sake of image."

I stare at Callahan and believe him. He's not the type to try and be something he isn't . . . and yet, that doesn't mean I'm not right on this. "Saving the environment is popular, Sharpe, so what's the harm in implementing visual signage around the property with subtle nods to what Ocean's Edge Resort is doing to further the cause?"

"We're supposed to be making more profit, not taking away from it."

"The resort already practices sustainability in various ways so let's point it out to our guests and add it to our marketing. In addition, Brady and I have been contacting local tour companies to find one that can customize a tour exclusively for our guests that will take them around the island to places and points that are of similar mind."

"Like?"

"Like the turtle sanctuary where they are breeding and reintroducing them back into the wild," I respond without hesitancy, knowing a man like Callahan needs to see utter confidence. "The nature reserve on the far side of the island. The—"

"No need to continue." He twists his lips as silence falls around us. "There's no perceived value there. There's no—"

"Signage is cheap. Custom tours add to our exclusivity. A fifteen percent kickback from the tour company adds to our profit."

"I still don't think it's appealing."

"I beg to differ."

"You always beg to differ. Personally, I just think you like to argue with me."

He's dismissing the idea. I can already see it, can already sense he's over this conversation, and both irritate the hell out of me. "No, I like to argue points, Callahan. Facts. And my experience, my job, tells me that this is a must across the board these days. Simple and boring but true."

"I don't see it. We own many resorts and—"

"And all of Sharpe International's properties have implemented ecotourism in one way or another in the past few months. Did you not know this?" His guarded stare should give me a warning. I don't heed it. I keep pushing. He wants to question me, then I'll damn well question him. "When was the last time you actually stayed at one of your properties like you're doing now? When was the last time you stepped out of your Manhattan tower and dirtied your hands so to speak?"

Callahan stares at me with an intensity I've yet to see from him before. His jaw is clenched and the muscles in his neck are taut.

It appears I hit a nerve.

"What's your point, Ms. Pierce?"

"*Ms. Pierce?*" I chuckle sarcastically. He's never called me that before. "Is that your way of putting me in my place and telling me you're pissed at me?"

His amber eyes are unwavering. "If I were putting you in your place, you'd know."

I move from where I'm standing near the window and walk to the other side of his office. I glance out the door into the larger office where my desk is and see a few stragglers packing up for the day. Desks get straightened. Lights get turned off. Good nights are murmured.

And soon, we'll be all alone in the office.

I need to get out of here to avoid any rumors arising about the two of us . . . *but* . . . Callahan has been testy all day. Combative and argumentative. It shouldn't be sexy. It should be off-putting. Unattractive.

And yet, it's had the exact opposite effect.

Even grumpy, he's insanely attractive. *And I'm turned on.* Needless to say, the underpants situation—or lack thereof—certainly hasn't helped.

I can't act on my attraction—that's a given. But if he opened the door with his stunt this morning, I might as well walk right through it and tease the hell out of him. Isn't that what Lizzy said in not so many words?

I turn to study Callahan. His hair is unruly today, his body tense. "What's eating you, Callahan?"

"Nothing."

"So you're just acting like an argumentative ass for no reason?"

"I didn't get much sleep last night," he says.

"I don't imagine you did considering you were stealing my panties and then scouring the island for their sturdy replacements."

"Anything for my girl." He smirks, clearly proud of himself, the mood suddenly shifting from tense to more playful. "They fit okay?"

"I wouldn't know." I quirk an eyebrow and return the smile as his eyes dart to my thighs and then back up. "Did you know there's a homeless outreach center on the east side of the island? Anyway, Rhonda at the front desk volunteers there on her days off, so I gave them to her to add to some of the other donations the staff has made."

"How charitable of you."

"You know me, always willing to give to those in need."

"And what about what I need?" He plays with the pen in his hand, but his eyes are locked on mine.

"I'm pretty sure you can handle your own needs just fine." I sell the lie despite the ache starting to burn within.

"Huh." His eyes dip to my cleavage, to my thighs, and then back up. "So what exactly are you wearing under that skirt of yours, then?"

Leaning over, I put my hands on his desk and whisper, "Absolutely nothing."

His eyes darken immediately, and I'm surprised the room doesn't ignite from the look alone.

"Take off your skirt," he orders in a low, even tone.

Jesus. If I didn't think he was sexy before, now, with those words, and his heated stare, I definitely would have.

I sink my teeth into my bottom lip. "No."

"You know I don't like to be disobeyed."

"This isn't the bedroom, Callahan." I take a step back and move over to the brown leather love seat in the far corner of the room. "You're not in control of me."

He shoves up from his chair and moves to the office door. He looks out into the now abandoned office before dimming the overhead lights, shutting the door softly, and turning the lock.

When he turns to face me again, I'm reminded of how turned on I was by his dominance that first night. "Take off your fucking skirt, Collins."

I offer a smile as I sink down onto the couch. "What happened to good, old-fashioned negotiations, huh?" My eyes veer to where he's already hard as a rock and pressing against the seam of his slacks.

"Sometimes you just have to take matters into your own hands." And now he repeats my words back to me.

"*Exactly*," I murmur as I lift my flowy skirt up and shift one of my legs onto the cushion beside me, spreading my thighs to give him the view of all views.

"Jesus fucking Christ," he groans, his fingers moving as if he's itching to touch. His eyes flicker from my pussy to my eyes then back down.

"Take out your cock," I order.

His eyes whip up to mine, his face a mask of surprise. "Excuse me?"

"You heard me. Take it out. Show me how hard I make you."

"What the fuck are you doing?"

"Giving you your brownie points for a great attempt at a good answer."

"But I was wrong?" His eyes track my hand as it rubs up and down my bare thigh.

"You *were* wrong." I move my hand between my thighs this time and let the pad of my finger rub over my clit. His hitched breath fills the room. "But don't worry, I'm a firm believer in keeping those you work with, those you want things from, incentivized to keep them trying harder."

"Is that so?" He starts to walk toward me, his hand finally pulling his cock free of his slacks.

"Uh-uh-uh."

"What?"

"I said incentivized. Not rewarded. Stay right there." I know I'm playing with fire. I invite the burn. "You can look, but baby, you can't touch."

"Sutton." My name is a strained warning from a desperate man.

"Hmm?" I lift an eyebrow and let a soft moan escape the back of my throat as I slide my fingers farther south.

"This is cruel." He chuckles but moves his hands over the head of his cock and back down as he stares at the movement of my fingers.

"But I'm not breaking any rules, right? It's not considered sleeping with my boss if we're not touching."

He groans. "Killing your boss is a crime too, though."

My breath stutters as I tuck my fingers into my wetness and then bring it back up to moisten my clit. "Stroke your cock, Callahan. Stroke it and let me watch you while you watch me."

He rolls his head back on his shoulders as he slides his hand up and back a few times. "You actually think this is a good way to get your panties back?"

"I don't care if I get them back." I moan and let my head fall back as I add more friction. "That just means you'll know I'm naked every time I pass by your desk. You'll know just what's within fingertips' reach when I slowly bend over to pick up a file that fell off my desk."

"Christ."

"Pure fucking torture," I say with a slight smirk. "Now stroke yourself."

An eyebrow raises but he does what I say anyway. His strong hand moves from the base of his shaft to the tip and back. It's mesmerizing to watch. Sexy. Arousing. Intoxicating in the most carnal of ways.

My fingers move faster, and it's a conscious thought to keep my eyes open so that I can watch him. Precum glistens his head and is then wiped away by his fingers.

"God, that's hot," I murmur as my fingers fly back and forth. "Are you thinking of me? Of sliding into me? Of pulling out and feeling me tighten around you begging for it to be back in?"

"Yes. Fuck, yes."

"Shh. Quiet," I moan and let my head fall to the side so I can both watch him and let my body push into the cushions.

"I don't fucking care if anyone hears me," he says.

"*Exactly.*" Our eyes meet across the short distance, my point more than made, but the high I'm chasing's still front and center.

"That's not what I—*Jesus*," he growls when I tuck my fingers back into myself and mimic what he's doing to his own cock.

"It feels so good, Callahan. So damn good."

"It's taking everything I have not to grab your ankles, yank you onto the carpet, and fuck you senseless."

Yes.

Please.

But I don't say a word. Can't. In this moment, I'm so aroused by him that I lose my sense of right and wrong. My defiance versus my compliance. My needs versus my wants.

My fingers rub faster.

His hand strokes harder.

Back and forth.

Up and down.

My body tightens and I grow even wetter. I'm on the verge of begging him to do as he threatened. Of yanking me down and fucking me senseless, but right as the words hit my lips, his groan fills the room.

I watch him come. His cock jerking in his hand as he spills in his other. And if that's not sexy enough, the look in his eyes—dark, dominant, desirous—as they lock on mine more than pushes me over the edge.

My orgasm hits me without a care for location or the need for silence. I bite the corner of the pillow as wave after wave washes through me. My breath is heavy and my body floating as I close my eyes and absorb its blissful wrath.

I yelp when Callahan's hands grasp my thighs, push against them to spread me wider, and his tongue licks its way between them. My body writhes under his touch as his tongue dips inside me.

His groan is everything. Part torture, part satisfaction.

"Callahan," I warn as I fist a hand in his hair to pull his head up.

A grin spreads over his arousal-glistened lips. "Can't blame a man for wanting to taste his brownie points."

"You're incorrigible." Pressing my foot to his chest, I push him back as I laugh.

"Guess number two?" he says, lying on his ass with his softening dick still hanging out of his trousers. "Learning the art of negotiation."

CHAPTER TWENTY-ONE

Sutton

"SO WE'VE EXPERIENCED FIVE OF THE TOP-TEN LIST SO FAR," Brady says, running a line through *Jeep ride adventures* on my tacked list to the bulletin board. "Thoughts?"

"My thoughts are that all five are feasible for Ocean's Edge. The question is, how do we adapt them to make them unique? Same goes with employment contracts."

"I spoke with Teresa today," Brady says about Sharpe International's employment contract lawyer.

"And?"

"We went through the employee requests item by item. I explained how they compare to other resorts here, as well as gave my opinion on which ones were dealbreakers. She's going to draw up a new contract so we have somewhere to start with Solomon," he says, referring to Ocean's Edge's employee representative.

"Good. That's great," I say. "I spoke to two interior designers today and have a call with one later to begin a renovation plan."

"Did you like either of the two you spoke with?"

"The first one not so much. Her mood board said contemporary modern over classic elegance and she fought me on that so she's a no-go. The second had some great ideas. We'll see what the third says and then make a decision by the end of the week. We need to get the ball rolling on that so plans can be submitted and materials ordered. The reno most likely will happen after my time here is up, but you'll have everything in place for a seamless process."

He snorts. "Seamless and renovation do *not* belong in the same sentence."

"I know, but one can hope," I murmur, getting distracted by an email that pops up on my screen from Roz in regards to our conversation earlier. "Oh, and ecotourism is a definite go."

"It is?" Brady looks up from his computer, his voice full of surprise as he lifts his chin toward Callahan's office. "You got the okay on it?"

A knowing smile slides across my lips. "We negotiated. *I won.*"

Brady does a double take and fist-bumps me across the desk. "Kicking ass and taking names. I like it." He does a little dance that has me laughing and then stills immediately.

I look over to see Callahan standing there, shoulder leaning against the doorway, hands shoved in his pockets, and his eyebrows raised.

Brady is frozen in place, and the sight of his raised eyebrows and mouth shocked into an "O" with the imposing figure of Callahan over his shoulder is comical.

"Something funny?" Callahan asks.

He heard me. I know he heard me, and it's written all over that gorgeous face of his.

"We were just celebrating. I was telling Brady that after some thorough negotiations, you agreed to let me move forward with the ecotourism signage as well as offering the customized tours for our guests."

"Some very thorough negotiations, indeed."

How can he look at me with such a measured, aloof expression when I can't even look him straight in the eyes without picturing him looking up at me from between my thighs the other night? In the office a few feet away, no less.

"Yes. Very."

"Well, the activities and the amenities are the easy part. You won on that round. Now we need to get to the hard part. Staff benefits, budget projections for salaries, and the costs for updating the décor."

"Yes, sir," I say. "Brady and I were just discussing that before you walked in."

"We were," Brady says with a nod.

"Good to see that you two are working well together," Callahan murmurs. "I also think it would be a nice touch to have homemade brownies delivered to every guest's room upon arrival as a welcome gift."

I all but choke on the sip of coffee I just took. "Brownies?"

He smirks when his eyes meet mine. "Yes. Brownies." He looks from Brady to me and then back. "Think of it as, what do they call it? *Brownie points*, if you will, for choosing to stay here."

"Brownie points?" Brady repeats.

"Exactly." A stoic nod of Callahan's head. "Keep up the good work. Carry on."

He walks out of the office like he does every afternoon to get a late workout in before heading to meetings or falling asleep on the chair in the villa with his laptop on his knees and spreadsheets fanned out across the table.

Staring at the door he just left through, I can't help but come to the realization that it's even harder to resist him than I originally thought.

I just have to keep reminding myself I don't care about him. Not his hard work or dedication here. Not the faraway look he gets in his eyes every once in a while when someone mentions his father. Not the raised voices I hear behind closed doors when a call from one of his brothers comes in.

And definitely not the fact that he keeps trying to answer my question when it's unanswerable to begin with.

CHAPTER TWENTY-TWO

Callahan

Ten Months Ago

"CAN YOU PLEASE GIVE US A MOMENT?" I LOOK UP AT GIL Diamante and his daughter Gia who are sitting at the table with us.

"For?" Gil asks.

"I need to speak with my father for a few moments," I say.

"Is something wrong?" Gia asks, those eyes of hers skimming over me suggestively.

"Nothing is wrong. We just need to discuss several points in private for a few moments," I explain.

"We'll find a place at the bar. You can find us there when you're finished." Gil stands up and pushes his chair in. "But don't keep us waiting long. I'm not a patient man, Mr. Sharpe."

I nod and then watch them move through the restaurant. The soft sounds of silverware on plates and muted conversation can be heard all around us.

My dad stares out the window of the restaurant to the twinkling lights of the city below us.

Everything about this feels wrong to me. The Diamantes. The meeting. The contract.

My dad.

"I know they brought the contract to try and salvage the deal, Dad, but we're sticking to our decision from earlier," I say, mentioning the meeting we had earlier with my brothers. "We're not signing it."

"Last I checked, I was the majority owner of this company." His smile holds no amusement when he offers it to me. It doesn't make what I have to do any easier.

"The projections for Ocean's Edge Resort aren't good. Ford and Ledger and the accountants have gone over them with a fine-tooth comb. They've spent days trying to make them work in our favor, but between the asking price and the cost needed to turn the resort around, we're looking at a considerable length of time to recoup our investment."

"I'm more than aware what the numbers are."

"Besides, it's far from being the Sharpe brand. It doesn't fit with our portfolio. It's—"

"Are you implying that if something isn't up to Sharpe expectations that we shouldn't put value in it?" He quirks an eyebrow, the reference to me and my screw-ups over time noted.

"Our point of this dinner tonight was to reject the deal. To walk away from it. Remember?"

He nods and looks at me, but a hollowness is in his eyes, and it feels like he really doesn't see me. It's been happening more and more these past few months.

He lifts his glass and takes a sip of his drink before pushing it away. "This isn't what I ordered. I don't even like scotch."

I glance at the drink and a sinking feeling hits me.

He's getting worse. What started as forgetting things every now and then is now becoming more frequent. Then there are holes in his memory about certain events in his life. Some days those moments are remembered, other days they are not.

He begged me to play it down to my brothers. Asked me to let him retain his dignity while he waited for the medication to do its trick, but it's harder than fucking hell to stand by and watch whatever it is, take piece after piece of him.

Including his favorite scotch.

"Dad?" I ask and wait for him to orient himself toward me. "What would you like to drink?"

"Scotch," he says. "You know what I like."

"It's right here," I say with a smile and push the glass he just rejected toward him.

He lifts it and takes a sip. "Perfection." He hums and closes his eyes as he savors the taste on his tongue. "Talk about hitting the spot."

When his eyes look back up to me, they are clear and lucid. I sigh in relief that the episode appears to be over and was shorter than most as of late.

"Good. I'm glad." I force a smile that I'm more than certain doesn't wash the concern from my eyes. He doesn't see it though because he's too busy staring at the contract on the table in front of him that I'm slowly pulling away from him and toward me.

"What are you doing?" he asks as he reaches out and puts a hand on the bound stack of papers, preventing me from taking it.

"We agreed not to accept their offer, did we not? You wanted to make a show of bringing the paper contract, sliding it across the table unsigned as a rejection. You said it was better this way," I explain. I don't know why we couldn't have done this in an email, but the man is as old-fashioned as old-fashioned can be. He'd make every deal a handshake if he could.

"Why would we do that when I want to sign the offer? I want to buy the property."

"Dad," I groan in frustration, more than pissed that I was left to babysit this dinner tonight. Technically he can cast the final vote as the majority shareholder so why the hell am I here anyway? *You have to protect Dad, Callahan. Protect him from making unsound business decisions. We're counting on you.* Ford's words were not subtle.

"Do you know that was where your mom and I took our honeymoon?"

"No, it wasn't. You went to—"

"I was there, I should know," he snaps in a way I haven't heard before. "I know I'm losing my mind, Callahan, but don't you dare tell me I don't know or remember this. It was your mother's choice, her pick, and I told her someday I was going to buy a patch of land there and make it everything she wanted. I failed her. I didn't do it when she was alive, but that doesn't mean I can't make amends now. That doesn't mean I can't still do it. Today is that day, son." He gets a soft, faraway look in his eyes and smiles. "Do you know I can still picture her standing on the beach with a flower in her hair, smiling at me, and posing for the camera?"

I study him, unsure what to say and uncertain if I remember correctly what had been said to me in the past.

What the fuck do I say?

How do I convince him otherwise when he seems so adamant he's right?

"Dad. We need to discuss your change of mind with—"

He reaches out and grips my forearm. "Give me this, son. Please. The company, the business, is what is helping to keep my mind clear. And I need to know while I still can remember that I fulfilled my promise to her." He squeezes. "No one else will understand this but you. Screw the numbers and projections and spreadsheets. Sometimes you have to go with your gut and your word."

His words hit hard. They're words my brothers won't understand or respect. *Just one more reason for them to treat me like shit.*

But I'll explain to them.

I'll make them understand what happened. Dad's reasoning.

"I'm all for going with your gut, but I'm certain we can hold out and negotiate a lower price to make up for the expense it will take to turn the resort into a Sharpe property."

"I'm dying, Callahan. I don't want to hold out. I want you to grant me this one, last wish. Of any of my three sons, you'd be the one to understand that while numbers don't lie, they aren't everything either." His eyes turn misty. "Please, son. Give me your blessing on this and grant me this one last thing."

Shit. That's the truth I don't want to face. I'd give anything to pretend I didn't hear them. Anything to make him live forever.

Anything to make him feel like he did right by his one true love.

"Okay." I whisper the word and hate the dread that eats at me.

We're a financially sound company that if the deal is shitty, we can sell and move on. We've done it before; we'll do it again. It's the nature of the beast.

"Okay?" His smile is the brightest and his eyes the clearest they've been in forever.

"Yes. Fine." But it's not. *It's so not.*

"Thank you. You're giving me the greatest gift anyone has ever bestowed upon me besides your mother giving me you three." He gives a soft smile. "I can't wait to tell her when I see her."

Tears burn my eyes and I hate that I feel like this is more than just a thank you. That this is a goodbye of some sort. I shake the thought and blame it on the discord eating at me.

The same discord that eats at me as I head toward the bar to tell the Diamantes we're ready to continue the meeting. This isn't the right financial decision. It's one made with the heart and not the head, but how do I say no to the man who has been the heart of this family for over thirty years? The one who has lifted me up even when I didn't deserve it? The one who has made all the sacrifices so that I can be sitting here at Eleven Madison Park, one of the most expensive restaurants in Manhattan, without batting an eye about the cost of the ensuing meal.

There is going to be hell to pay for this, for allowing this to happen, but . . . *I can't wait to tell her when I see her.*

Jesus fucking Christ.

"Mr. Diamante, sir," I say when I see him standing at the bar with a drink in hand. "Sorry for the delay, but we're ready to proceed."

"Proceed?" he asks. "Because I feel like you've been toying with me. I'm a busy man who doesn't like to be led on. I never intended to sell Ocean's Edge until your father pursued me doggedly. This isn't a must-sell for me, Callahan. In fact it's far from it. But I like your dad. I don't understand him, but I like him. So don't invite me to fly here and have a discussion and then make me wait. I've pulled deals from a table for less than that."

And with that, Gil Diamante walks past me, toward the table.

"Can I get you something, Mr. Sharpe?" Sam, the usual bartender, asks.

I need something strong to wash the bad taste from my mouth. "Yes. *Please.* A shot of your choice." I glance around. "I'm going to run to the restroom. I'll be right back."

"Yes, sir."

The bathroom is empty when I enter it and just as I unzip my fly, the door opens at my back.

And I hear the click of heels.

When I turn to look, Gia Diamante is standing there with a smirk and desire firing in her eyes.

I stuff my cock back in my slacks and turn to face her as I zip up, although the look on her face says she'd prefer I keep it out.

"I'm assuming you know you're in the wrong bathroom," I say, taking a step toward the sink to wash my hands.

"Just like I assume you know where I'm staying this evening." She takes a step closer. "Once the deal is signed, I would love to show you . . . my appreciation for your assistance in making your dad accept the deal."

"Your appreciation, huh?"

Her siren's smile is seductive. Her fingernail that scrapes up the front of my cloth-clad cock even more so. "I have *a lot* of appreciation," she whispers.

"So this is how the Diamantes close deals?" If it is, maybe I should be more involved in closing them.

Her laugh is throaty as she leans in and tugs on my earlobe with her teeth causing my balls to draw up. "I'll let you know once it's closed," she whispers before she turns on her heel and leaves the bathroom.

I have to wait a second for my hard-on to abate before I leave the bathroom. When I do, Sam is sliding my shot across the bar with a smirk.

CHAPTER TWENTY-THREE

Callahan

"SOME PEOPLE NOT HAPPY, MAN," KEONE SAYS IN HIS DISTINCT island accent as he pours a draft beer.

"Why's that?" I ask.

"Just hearing rumblings."

"About?" I ask, already dreading this conversation and it hasn't even really started.

"They giving raises over at some of the other resorts."

"But we offer better medical benefits."

"That only matters, man, if they sick. It doesn't help pay the rent though." He holds up a finger and walks to the other end of the bar to take an order.

I close my eyes and take a deep breath.

This is the last fucking thing we need here. I'd like to think we're slowly getting shit in order. *Slowly.* Brady is a little kooky, but the man is a godsend when it comes to wrangling all the things Sutton is implementing while managing the staff at the same time.

It allows me to immerse myself in the bullshit numbers so I can get this over and done with. So I can walk the fuck away. From the resort and the family business.

There's a grass shack on a beach somewhere that's calling my name. One where cell service is scant, the surf is strong, and the days stretch forever.

I take another sip of beer and wonder what my dad would think in this situation. My brothers forcing me to be here. Their insistence that I physically manage instead of manage from afar like they do.

Don't get your hands dirty, Callahan. That's what you hire people for. You have to be felt but not seen, heard without having to scream, strong but not be an asshole.

Well, I've definitely failed that last part, haven't I?

And the irony that Sutton threw in my face that I don't get my hands dirty while my dad used to tell me not to isn't lost on me.

But maybe she's right. Maybe being made to feel like an idiot over not knowing we'd implemented ecotourism as a part of our resort portfolio is a prime example of why I don't belong here in the first place.

And yet here I am. Trying to give life to something our father so desperately wanted. The funny thing is I thought it would hurt more being here. That being at a place he was so hell-bent on purchasing would make me sad.

It's done just the opposite.

Sure I want the fuck out of here as soon as my time here, my penance, has been served, but it's not so bad on the whole.

And doesn't that have everything to do with Sutton?

Christ.

When have I ever let a woman lead me around by the balls without at least a little squeeze now and then?

Never.

Fucking never.

And yet when I leave the bar, she's still on my mind. She's so much easier to focus on than the constant texts from Ledger and Ford demanding status reports and updates.

If they want to really know, they'll show up and find out the status themselves. They'll probably dismantle every single thing we've done just to say I've done it wrong in the process.

Spite is a mean, nasty bitch and they have it in fucking spades.

I walk for a bit. Down paths I've walked a hundred times before, but this time without my head buried in my phone.

Ocean's Edge is beautiful. It's the perfect location, the right setup, let's just hope what Sutton and I are doing is *enough*.

But enough for what? To appease my brothers? To really flip this around? To feel like I truly fulfilled the promise to my dad? To . . . *what?* Now that I've been forced here, what exactly do I want out of this other than it being my last resort?

A couple chases each other down the beach and shrieks. I watch their silhouettes against the moonlit sky and smile. Did my mom and dad really dig their toes in the sand here? Did they play in the water and fall deeper in love with this place as their backdrop?

I have no clue, but I'm pretending they did. I'm pretending that my dad had a moment of clarity, of remembering this place, and that my decision to let him buy it was the right one. That just like the dementia stole his mind from us, it didn't also steal that one last moment that I thought was real.

The lights are on in the villa when I get home. *Home?* That's what this is to me now? Maybe that's what it feels like. Coming home to her. Knowing she's actually there for once. Maybe waiting for me.

Maybe wanting me.

I know she's purposely made herself scarce when I'm here. She even jokes around the office about her absence to try and prevent the inevitable chatter that she's sleeping with her boss.

I'm wishing that chatter was correct right about now.

I move toward her room where the door is open and the light is on. She's sitting cross-legged on the bed in a tank top and shorts, her hair wet, her skin still pink from a hot shower. She has a pencil between her teeth as she types away at something on her laptop.

Jesus. When is she not stunning?

"Honey, I'm home," I say.

Her eyes flash up to me and a soft smile adds warmth to them. "Hello, dear. How was your day?" she asks as she takes the pencil from her mouth and sets it down on the nightstand.

"The usual. Don't you ever stop working?" I ask as I walk into her room and fall face first onto her bed.

"We have a lot to do in a short amount of time," she says as I turn my face and look at her. Of course, right in front of me is her bare thigh as a temptation of what I can't touch. "I don't have any time to waste. Besides you're not paying me to rest on my laurels."

Turning on my side, I prop my head up on my elbow. "No, but I'm also not working you to the bone." I push her laptop with my finger. "We've been here a month, and I don't know anything about you outside of work stuff."

"That's a lie," she says wryly, but she closes her laptop and moves it to the table beside her. "You know what kind of panties I wear." She quirks a brow, thinking she's being witty but when I just continue to stare at her, she sighs. "Fine. What do you want to know?"

"Where are you from? Where are you going? Something in between," I say.

"That's an awful lot of 'personal' for a man who doesn't like to mix with his employees," she says but there is a playful quality to her voice that says she doesn't mind. I hadn't thought when I walked in here that I'd be asking her these questions either, but it would be a lie if I said I wasn't intrigued by her. How did she become so . . . *talented? Intuitive?*

And she's not wrong. I rarely get invested in employees . . . or women I want to fuck.

"You're teaching me to change my ways." I smile. "What's in it for you is a much nicer Callahan Sharpe."

"Too late. I already know that," she whispers as she reaches out and runs her fingernails through my hair and over my scalp. I close my eyes and lean into her touch.

"You're going to put me to sleep."

"Either that will or information about me will because I'm not a very interesting person."

I snort. "I doubt that."

"I'm not."

"I want to know, anyway."

"Okay," she murmurs as her fingers continue to work their magic. "I was born in a small town in Upstate New York. Nothing remarkable about my childhood other than I couldn't wait to turn eighteen so I could escape the everyday fighting in my house. My parents were alcoholics who cared more about the next bottle than worrying about making sure their daughter was prepared for life."

"I'm sorry."

"Don't be." She offers a soft smile that says please don't pity me. "I had some money I'd received in inheritance after my grandmother died—she was the glue of the family and I knew with her gone, things would only get worse. So I took that money and I left. Found my way to Brooklyn where I roomed with three other college students. Went to college and got my degree while I was working as a gofer for Resort Transition Consultants. I slowly worked my way to the front desk, then to an associate, then a junior account manager, and on and on until . . . this."

"I'm impressed," I say with all sincerity because in my world, people don't work their way up. They are born into it. Handed it. But Sutton is so very different. "Truly. That explains why you know the ins and outs of every facet. And your family?"

She shrugs. "Is it bad if I say that they are my parents and I care for them as my parents, but them not being in my life is the best thing that I've been able to do for myself?"

I nod, but don't understand in the least. Yes, my brothers are currently being assholes to me, but growing up we were always united as a family. Even if it wasn't easy trying to live up to the Sharpe name, we had each other.

Maybe that's why what they're doing now hurts so much. Dad is gone. Shouldn't we be unifying instead of pulling apart?

Is that why I'm here instead of at my grass shack? To honor our father, but also to maybe win back some of what we were? To get my best friends back?

I sigh softly and focus on the feeling of her fingers scratching my scalp. It's easier to not think about it. Easier to want and wish than to worry and wonder.

"What else did you ask?" she asks as I look over to her where she's twisting her lips and looking down at me. "*Where am I going?* At some point, when I get enough experience, I'd like to branch out and start my own firm. I think there's something to be said about the risk and reward of finding clients and taking on their projects for myself."

"I can understand that." I reach out and draw a lazy finger up and down the line of her thigh. "Tell me about your ex."

"My ex?"

"Yes. He's the reason we met after all, right?" I smile and grab a pillow to pull under my head. It smells like her shampoo. "Shouldn't I know about the schmuck who didn't do a good enough job to keep you?"

Her eyes soften as she chews the inside of her cheek. "Can I say I was lonely and naïve and did everything wrong and leave it at that?"

"I doubt that."

"When no one has taught you how to love, Callahan, you take the first sign of affection sent your way and cling to it even when it's not healthy." Her eyes dip and study her fingers moving through my hair. Her shame is written all over her face, and it guts me to see it. "I'm not proud of it, of staying with him for as long as I did when he preferred me to fail rather than flourish for his own ego's sake. But I'm proud of myself for walking away from it. It didn't hurt this opportunity came along at the perfect time to do just that."

I hate that my gut twists at the thought of another man touching her. Of another man hurting her. "And sometimes I think things happen at the right time just when we need it most."

What the hell does that mean, Cal? You're not talking about her, right?

There's no way you're talking about her.

"And as far as everything in between, I think I'm still figuring that out as I go." She gives a definitive nod as if she's content with her answer. "What about you, Callahan? Tell me about you."

Christ. I opened that door, didn't I?

CHAPTER TWENTY-FOUR

Sutton

"WHAT DO YOU WANT TO KNOW?"

"How about I ask the most obvious thing since your expression says you'd rather die than talk about yourself." I laugh. His wince tells me he is not a fan of the tables being turned. Too bad. I want to know more about this man who fills my thoughts and then plops onto my bed unannounced out of the blue. I lob a softball at him for a warmup. "Should I assume you don't have a girlfriend since you pick women up in clubs and are currently shacking up with a woman? A rather hot woman, I might add, but a woman—"

"A very hot woman, indeed."

"That didn't answer the question."

He chuckles. "No. I don't have a girlfriend."

"Is that by design or because you've yet to find *the one?*"

"It's just how it is." He lifts his eyebrows. "Right. Wrong. I don't know. I don't like complicated."

"Says the man who was thrown into the most complicated situation ever when I walked in the door of that conference room."

He laughs and it makes me smile. "Complicated yes, but I definitely wasn't complaining that I got to see you again."

Something happens in my tummy at those words, and I try to ignore the silly, feminine response to hearing them. The flip-flop of it. The fluttering inside.

To know it wasn't dread filling him at the sight of me but rather pleasure.

For the first time since we've been here, I feel nervous being near him. Flustered and uncertain how to respond, I change topics. "Is it true what they say about multiples? That they are the best of friends and can read each other's thoughts."

"I tell you I was happy to see you again and you counter with questions about my brothers? That's harsh."

I chuckle. "Well . . ."

He flops back onto his back, the sigh he emits almost ominous as he fixates his stare on the ceiling. "That's a complicated answer," he finally says.

"Family always is, right?"

I give him the silence to work through the emotions dancing through his eyes and immediately regret asking what I thought would be a no-brainer question.

"The simple answer is yes. We *can* complete each other's sentences." He pauses and there is a sadness that falls over his features that makes my heart break. "I still consider them my best friends."

"And the complicated answer?" My voice is gentle, fingers brushing the waves of hair off his forehead reassuring. And it surprises me how relaxed I am with him. I don't think I ever did this with Clint—talked and touched him with this level of gentle intimacy.

I care about Callahan Sharpe.

More than I think I even want to admit to myself.

"The complicated answer is that my dad favored me and that has damaged my relationship with my brothers now that we're older." He scrubs a hand over his jaw. "Long story short, our mother died when we were in our teens. Nothing long and tragic, she just didn't wake up one morning from a heart attack she had in her sleep."

"I'm so sorry." My heart hurts for him, for the pain in his voice.

He shrugs despite the obvious grief. "She was the love of his life." The ghost of a smile and flicker of his eyes over to me is so bittersweet. He clears his throat. "I'm the one who's the most like her. My demeanor, my mannerisms, my everything."

"And so he clung to you to hold her close."

"I'm thinking a psychologist would agree with that statement." Another shrug, his discomfort more than obvious. "And while in any situation that wouldn't have gone over well with my brothers, what made it worse, is I was the screw-up Sharpe. The one who didn't live up to the expectations set for us. Ford and Ledger were penalized for every step outside of the lines, while I did so freely and blatantly. The difference was my transgressions, my fuck-ups, were often overlooked."

"Animosity. Resentment. Jealousy," I murmur trying to picture the dynamic and remembering the tension I felt between them that first day.

He chuckles. "Believe me, a lot of the time, their feelings are well deserved. I'm not an angel and probably exploited my father's forgiveness way more than it was deserved, but yes, there is a lot of resentment for it."

Callahan goes on to explain situations here and there where he was given an out while his brothers were held to the fire. His crashing the car but Ledger getting in trouble for letting him get behind the wheel. His dropping out of Wharton and how what his brothers saw as favoritism, really ended up being his own personal hell. His screwing up a major deal because of a missed error.

I can see where his brothers have issues, but I can also see times Callahan tried to force his dad to see the blatant differences in affection (if you could call it that). I respect him for admitting, right or wrong, that at times he accepted this preferential treatment as a way to escape punishment.

But to me it sounds like his punishment was handed out, just in different ways.

"We all loved our dad differently, just like he loved us differently. It's not right or wrong, it was just as it was. And I think our father's death could have brought us closer together, that my brothers would have let it all pass, had I not advocated for this deal to buy Ocean's Edge."

"Why was this a bad thing?"

"It's a long story but it would take too much to turn this place around into the high-end resort consistent with the Sharpe brand. My brothers pored over projections and budgets, and God knows what, but the exponential disbursements to bring it to where it needs to be wasn't cost effective."

"Why am I just hearing this now? Aren't I supposed to be the one in the know so I can give my client what they want?" I laugh but it lacks humor. "In my opinion, you'd recoup the costs, but it would take some time, yes."

"And in the meantime, bring down the value of the Sharpe portfolio that we rely on as leverage for loans to buy several other properties in the works."

"So why are you here then? Why not sell it off?"

He tells me about the meeting with the owners. About his dad's wishes, his request for this one thing. How he granted it because he couldn't say no. And then the fallout with his brothers after.

"You were in a horrible position. They actually blamed you for it?"

He nods. "It didn't help that I fell off the grid after he died. I spent my time traveling here and there, anywhere that didn't remind me of him."

"And now of course you've been forced to come here where you'd think you'd be thinking about him all the time."

"It's been good and bad . . . but honestly, I think they were right. I think I got so caught up in the moment, in knowing he was slipping away, that I bought anything the dementia told me, because there's nothing here visually that I've seen in the pictures I've sifted through of him and my mom. But it doesn't matter though because the damage is done . . ."

He talks of his brothers' ultimatums and the possibility of being forced out of his spot in the family business. Of the fight they had that day I left the conference room.

"So this isn't what you want to be doing with your life?" I ask, partially joking, partially honest.

His groan is the sound of frustration. "I've never been given the option to do anything else." He looks at me and the emotion swimming in his eyes allows me to see him in a different light. He's not just the cocky, arrogant man I first met at Club Coquette. There's more to the man. So much more. "My goal was to finish this project and walk away."

"Your last resort."

"Yep. My *last resort.*"

"Wait. Seriously?" I ask, his complete nonchalance throwing me. "You're seriously going to walk away, *away?*"

He nods but his expression doesn't look as confident as his nod is. "Yes. If my dad's death taught me anything it was to live life to its fullest. I want to travel. I may have walked away from the strict confines and rubrics of Wharton but that doesn't mean I've ever wanted to stop learning. I just want to do it by experiencing things outside of the life I grew up in."

I stare at Callahan with his hair mussed and his smile soft. I'm surprised by his answer. I'd think a man of his stature would occupy rooms at the Four Seasons between jaunts on a private jet.

174

"Your answer surprises me."

He shrugs. "Good surprise or bad surprise?"

"It just doesn't seem to fit the image I have of you."

"I'm a man of many talents," he teases.

There are so many things I want to ask him. Where do you want to travel? How long would you do it for? Would traveling really fulfill that natural, determined drive I see in him when he's at work?

He may not like it, but you can't just turn those kinds of personality traits off like a switch.

I don't ask any of the questions though because granted, he is talking to me, but that doesn't mean his book is open to be read page by page.

So I ask the most obvious of all my questions.

"But by doing that—by walking away—wouldn't that prove to your brothers everything they insinuate? That you don't care about the family business? That what your dad built was all for naught? That—"

"I suffocate in office buildings, Sutton."

"You're not suffocating here, though."

He angles his head to the side and the shyest smile slides onto his lips. "Surprisingly, no, I'm not." He looks down to where his hand is resting on my thigh and stares at it for a beat before bringing his eyes back up to mine. "This has been different."

"More hands-on."

"Yes."

"It's different when you get to see the changes you're making versus only analyzing them on a spreadsheet."

"It does."

I study him. The soft lines in his face. The sun-kissed skin. The rough cut of his jaw. The wave of his hair. *This man was not made for corporate life.* "I have a feeling you've reached your personal sharing limit for this evening." I smile. "So why are you in my bed, making it very hard for me to work, Mr. Sharpe?"

"Because mine is lonely." He pouts like a little boy, and I'd be lying if it's not taking everything I have not to lean over and kiss him.

"So you think if you come and occupy mine, Mr. Brownies-In-Every-Room, that you won't be so lonely."

An unapologetic grin lights up his face. "Can't blame a guy for trying."

"I'm impressed. It's taken you a whole month before going the direct route," I tease.

"We're never here together."

"By design." I shrug. "You're always off wheeling and dealing or whatever you're doing at night."

"I'm schmoozing. Trying to negotiate prices and up our discounts since costs on the island are so high."

I try not to let my surprise show. I had no clue. The businessperson in me wants to ask all the details, but the woman in me, the one who is highly attracted to the man beside me, keeps it light. "And here I thought you were out having torrid love affairs with all the island girls."

"It's crossed my mind."

"Hey!" I pick up the pillow beside me and hit him on the head with it. In seconds, he's tickling me and we're wrestling for control. Laughter fills the room as I struggle against his strength that he's willfully seceding to me, until I end up on top of him, straddling his hips.

My sides hurt from laughing so hard as I pin his hands to either side of his head in mock victory.

And all is fun and games until he stops resisting. I look down to see him looking up at me, his expression so very serious as the smile slowly fades from his lips.

The flutters turn into full-blown flapping wings.

"Callahan," I murmur.

"Sutton," he whispers. And that's when I see how vulnerable he's made himself to me. Perhaps he's due one of my truths as well. *Honesty.*

"For the record, I was happy to see you again too."

His eyes darken, his smile is ever so slight. He reaches out and cups the back of my neck as warning bells go off in my head.

"Just . . ." He sighs as his eyes dart down to my lips. "I won't cross your line . . ." His expression is pained, his words hesitant, as I resist when he tries to pull me toward him.

"I . . ."

"Just let me kiss you. It's been a shit day. Don't I at least get that much?"

Our eyes meet and this time, when he pulls on my neck, I press my lips to his.

The kiss is gentle in nature when all we've ever been is hunger and fire. It's a slow, seductive touch of lips and tongues and soft sighs of unspoken words.

He stays true to his word and doesn't try to advance the kiss despite the deep ache I feel that I know he feels too.

It's just my fingers linked with his against the mattress. Just our mouths moving tenderly at a leisurely pace. Just two people reveling in the simple yet overrated act of kissing.

"Sutton," he groans and squeezes my hands.

I rest my forehead against his, our panted breaths filling the space between. "I know. *I know*."

"It's probably best if I go back to my cold, lonely bed." He chuckles painfully.

"Probably." But when I shift off him, I keep my leg hooked over his thigh and my arm around his waist.

"You have an iron will, Collins, because I've gotta be honest, you're killing me slowly."

I give a smile he can't see as we lie like this, tangled together, until his breathing evens out and his soft snore fills the room.

An iron will?

Hardly.

But I think Callahan Sharpe just got to me by doing exactly the opposite of what I expected.

By respecting me and my wishes.

Was that the answer I was looking for?

I don't know . . . but it feels pretty damn close.

I can tell myself to stick to my guns all I want, but he's gotten to me. I thought he was all rough edges with a hard, sexy exterior, but there's definitely more to him than that.

CHAPTER TWENTY-FIVE

Sutton

HE'S GOOD AT THIS.

He might not think he is, but he's a natural at putting people at ease (when he wants to) and getting his point across.

I don't blame him for finding the day-to-day boring or suffocating or whatever he called it the other night. But I do find it odd he feels this way. As I sit and watch him talk to the Ocean's Edge employee representative, he looks like this is something he does every day.

My mind veers to the other night. Falling asleep in his arms. Waking up and studying him as he slept. The lines relaxed on his face. The thick lashes fanned against his cheeks. The dark stubble from a night of growth. It took everything I had not to reach out and touch him. To kiss him. To go back on everything I've stood for so far.

I forgot the ease of a getting-to-know-you conversation. The flutter in your belly when a man looks at you and how his gaze feels like fingers gliding over your skin. Of that quickening of your pulse as his rumbly laugh vibrates through you.

And that's what the other night felt like. Getting to know each other.

We jumped right to sex, and now that I'm getting to know Callahan better, I truly do like him beyond the flirting and sexual tension that coils in every room we occupy.

The question is, what do I do about it, because at the end of the day, my dilemma remains the same. He's my boss. I'm in his employ. And if someone finds out we are anything more than that, my job, my credibility, my morality, is compromised. I have worked far too hard and for far too long to let anything derail my professional trajectory. I'm twenty-six years old with my mind set on starting my own company.

Does it really matter though when it feels like he's been avoiding me since?

It's only been a few days.

The man is busy.

Quit overthinking.

But it feels like more than that. Like something has shifted.

"That's Sutton's thought as well," Callahan says, pulling my attention back to the conversation at hand. "After looking at the employment contracts of some of the other resorts, we added that back in."

"This was your doing?" Solomon asks in his Caribbean accent with narrowed eyes in my direction. "Forgive me, but I find that most consultants are just overpaid delegators. No offense, of course."

I nod. "None taken. While we're a long way from making final decisions on the entirety of the employment package, this is where we currently stand. We'd like you to look at the contract and make notes for our consideration."

Callahan all but winces at the last comment. We went round after round last night with Brady and a few other managers over how much weight we should allow Solomon on this. But if he's speaking collectively for the majority of the employees, then we definitely need to take his input into account.

Or at least let him *think* we do.

"We do have a list of demands." His smile is smug if not taunting, and I'm more than certain that Callahan's hand under the desk is fisting.

"As I expected," Callahan says smoothly. "But as I stated already, Sharpe International is a non-union entity. Therefore, we can take what you request into account, but that doesn't mean we have to agree to the demands."

"You'd be silly not to. There are a dozen resorts on this island offering jobs right now," Solomon says as he leans back and folds his hand over the folder in front of him.

"Just as there always have been," Callahan counters rather icily. "Like I said, Mr. Freeman, please take a look at our tentative working copy. We can meet again next week to discuss your opinions."

Their stares hold and unspoken challenges are exchanged. I question if I should interject, add some niceties to the sudden tension, but decide against it.

"Well then." Callahan scoots his chair back and stands, making sure he remains in control of the situation. "Until next time."

"Until next time then." Solomon stands slowly, deliberately, and nods in goodbye. "Gia told me to tell you hi."

Callahan freezes. It's slight and most likely would go unnoticed to anyone else, but the hitch is there.

"She said she looks forward to seeing you again while you're here." Solomon offers a smarmy expression, almost as if he knows something Callahan doesn't. But before Callahan can say anything else, Solomon is out the door.

"Prick," Callahan mutters under his breath.

"Gia, huh?" I cross my arms over my chest and lift a brow playfully. "See? I was right. You're out having torrid love affairs all around the island with mystery women."

"I have meetings, Sutton. Dinner meetings. Client meetings. All kinds of fucking meetings that are so damn boring they make my ears want to bleed." He waves a hand at me as if I'm dismissed. I sit there stunned. *What the hell?* And why does the mere mention of another woman's name eat at me? "There are women in some of the meetings. None in others. I don't really think I have to explain myself to you."

"No one said you did," I say, surprised by his demeanor. That, in and of itself, already has my mind running a million miles an hour to the point where "Gia" and Callahan are already riding away in the sunset and living happily ever after. "I was just—"

"Yeah. I know." He stacks his papers up and shoves them under his arm. "I've got meetings," he says without meeting my eyes and walks out without saying another word.

I stare at the door he just exited and sigh.

Okaaaay. Perhaps I haven't been imagining his distance these last few days. Perhaps he regrets his openness from the other night. *What had I expected? That we'd be . . . moving forward?*

Is there really anything we would be moving toward?

CHAPTER TWENTY-SIX

Sutton

"NO. IT'S LIKE WE HAD THAT GREAT NIGHT OF KISSING, THEN the weird meeting where he kind of exploded on me, and now ... Now it's like we're in the same spots at the same times but we don't really see each other."

"How is that even possible? You're supposed to be working together," Lizzy says.

"We are ... but it's not exactly like we're talking about anything other than resort matters. He spends a lot of time in his office behind closed doors talking with people back home about the financial aspects, looking at budgets and whatnot. Things I only need to know the end result of. I mean, we're getting down to a few weeks left so ... I don't know. Maybe beyond that, he's checked out."

"I doubt he's checked out. If he were, he'd be out on the beach with a rum punch in hand like you should more often."

"I have one in hand right now. Does that make you happy?" I ask and take a sip of it.

"So let me see. You're working side by side without really talking and at night you're not seeing each other."

"Right. At night he's usually at dinner meetings elsewhere on the island with who knows who."

"Ah, so this is the Gia aspect."

"Oh my God," I groan. "I sound like a jealous bitch when I have no right to be jealous. I mean, maybe I played too hard to get so he moved on? Maybe I—"

"Maybe you need to stop sounding like a needy girlfriend for a second so we can dissect this slowly," Lizzy says in her no-bullshit voice.

And this is why I love her.

"Yes. You're right. Please, dissect away while I have another sip of my drink."

"Sip away." She chuckles. "So clearly Callahan is a busy man."

"Yes."

"And you feel like after the other night—the kissing and that's it—that he's distanced himself from you."

"Either that or I'm overthinking and reading into *everything*."

"Which is highly likely because, *hello*, we're females."

"True. Yes. I don't know," I groan. "It's like we had this great night where we really got to know each other, to enjoy each other without that tension that makes you feel like you're constantly on edge. I thought maybe we'd turned a corner and that . . . I don't know what but—"

"But you feel it and it's valid because you feel it," she says as I give a nod she can't see. "And he talked about himself in depth, and you talked about yourself in depth and so you both kind of made yourselves vulnerable."

"I guess."

"So it's only natural for a guy to pull back and feel like a sap after something like that. At least in my experience."

"So that's good then . . . but . . ."

"What are you not saying, Sutt?"

"We kissed, and then we stopped."

"Which is what you asked for. So a guy who respected your wishes," she says like it's a shocking thing. "Why do you make it sound like it's a bad thing?"

I struggle with how to say words that feel perfectly valid in my head but suddenly feel stupid when I put a voice to them. "*But why?* If he wants me so badly, why stop there? He didn't even try to talk me into doing more like he has in the past. Is that because he was simply placating me to not hurt my feelings when in reality he's moved on and is already screwing someone else here?"

"*She said she looks forward to seeing you again while you're here.*"

Gia.

The name floats through my brain and I hate that it does. He was so defensive the other day about her. *Has he already been screwing her? That would explain why he stopped at kissing me.* He's getting what he wants somewhere else now. With no restrictions. Why can't I help latching on to that . . . suspicion and not let go?

"Whoa. Let's back up some, shall we?" She laughs, completely justifying my own rationalization that I'm crazy.

"Sorry. It's been bottled up inside and that's just making it all worse so—"

"So that's why you called me."

"Yes."

"Personally, I think the man is still into you. I think he's met his match who won't drop her panties at the first flash of his pretty smile—well except for that first time of course, but we're excluding that. And considering how much you've cock-teased the hell out of him, I'm rather impressed with his restraint."

"I have not cock-teased him," I say just for good measure. I feel like being around the man is a tease, every minute of every day.

"You're so full of shit. Of course, you have with your whole 'what's in it for me' schtick—"

"It's not a schtick. It's—"

"Valid. Yes, I know." She sighs. "I agree that it is. I even agree that he needs to understand that by being with him, you're risking everything . . . but maybe that's what happened. Maybe so far he's seen you as Sexy, Siren Sutton who comes on his command, and now after your discussion the other night, after getting to know the real you, he sees you as Sensible, Sweet Sutton with real-life problems, issues, and shock of all shocks, emotions."

"He's the one who finagled his way into living in the same villa with me. He had to have expected we'd have actual conversations during the time we were here. Conversations with words other than *which position do you want to try next*."

"Agreed," she murmurs. "But he is a guy, a player if we're guessing right, so other than in the bedroom, I don't exactly think your needs are high on his priority list."

I open my mouth to defend him and then shut it. Why do I feel like maybe they are high on his list, that he does see me as more than sex, when three weeks ago I would have absolutely agreed with her and laughed while I did so?

"Perhaps," I finally murmur.

"I'm just trying to figure him out. The man is intrigued by you for sure. I mean, there has to be more to it than you're a challenge and that's it because, let's be honest, he could snap his fingers and have anyone he wants."

"And you don't think I know that?" I laugh as I push against the ground so my hammock chair twists me weightlessly around.

"That doesn't mean you change course, Sutt. It means you stick to your guns."

"Clearly you haven't had sex with him before. He's a pretty potent drug to resist."

"I'm sure he is, but you resisted the other night, right? You kissed and made out and there is something to be said for that in and of itself. The intimacy. The vulnerability. So take that as a small victory and then I say make him keep working for those moments. Make him think of you as a potent drug too. Truth be told, I think he already does."

"I disagree."

"He's still coming around, Sutton, when other guys would have been long gone. To be honest, in this short amount of time, he's brought out a confidence in you that I haven't seen in forever. There's something to be said for that. So don't let this lapse in him taking a step back—in regrouping—deter you. You need to keep that confidence going. You need to tease and flirt and really believe that no matter how good he is, you're worth more."

"Lizzy . . ." She's right. I know she's right, and yet I hate this sudden feeling of uncertainty, as if I'm in over my head.

"Sexual frustration is the best foreplay there is. Make him think about you, daydream about you, be desperate for you."

"Isn't that just playing a game when the end result is a foregone conclusion?"

"You were already playing the game so what's the difference? I say it's more of letting him know your worth."

"What happened to Ms. You-Can-Have-Sex-Without-Strings?"

"She's still here. It's still a good option. But that doesn't mean he doesn't have to value the experience." She falls quiet. "Besides, there's nothing wrong with cock-teasing the hell out of him while you see how he is with other people there. That'll be your real judge of whether he'll guard the secrecy of your sexcapades."

I close my eyes and let the breeze tickle over my cheeks as I think about Lizzy and her advice and my desire to sleep with Callahan again. The silence stretches as I mull over everything she's just said. The truth in it. The truth I need to own.

"You like him, don't you," she says softly.

I give a half laugh. "I do, Lizzy. More than I expected to and I don't know if it's too soon after Clint or just because he's so different than him . . . but I do and . . ." And I fear Callahan Sharpe has more of a chance of hurting me emotionally than Clint ever did.

How is that even possible?

Maybe that's my hesitation.

"I know you do. I've read it in your texts. I can hear it in your voice. And I want you to hear me when I say to you, there's nothing wrong with it. Nothing. Sometimes the right people are put in your path when you need them the most. Maybe Callahan is that right person."

"You know I feel like an idiot, right? That I'm *in like* with my one-night rebound stand?"

"Worse things could happen. Like you like him first and then find out the sex is terrible." She laughs. "That would be a bummer."

"True. Very true." I emit a long sigh. "So now what? Do I just let go of the whole *what's in it for me* thing?" I ask, suddenly feeling stupid and juvenile for even suggesting it to Callahan. I know I panicked and was trying to keep my morality in check.

"*Absolutely not.* He needs to answer the question because he needs to think about stuff like that. And honestly, it doesn't matter if he does or doesn't figure out the answer. What matters is that *you* figure it out, Sutton, because it's a question you should ask yourself of every situation, relationship, anything that you're in. Even if the answer is simply *to feel good.*"

"But—"

"But nothing," she scolds. "The answer is probably going to change too, and that's okay. What you're looking for one day might be different than what you're wanting to get out of something two weeks from now. You're the keeper of that secret answer and the mover of that bar, so it's no one's business if you've moved it, okay?"

My head swims with the truth in her words and the desire to find again that confidence I came here with. I let one man take it from me before. I will not let another one do it again simply because I may have given too much information about my past. *Is that what's happening here?* Am I hearing Clint's voice in my ear, goading me, suggesting no other man will want me because of where I come from? Who I am? No. Lizzy's right. Even if Callahan has moved on, I will not believe it's because I'm not worthy of his interest. *His loss.* And if he is still interested? I will keep flirting, because why the hell not?

"Thank you for the pep talk, the cheerleading, and the advice."

"Any time. You know that." The affection in her voice makes me feel loved. "Do me one favor, though?"

"Of course. Yes."

"Don't leave that chair you're swinging in until you figure out the answer to your question and the first rung for that bar to sit at. Remember, it can move at any time and that's perfectly fine."

"Okay."

"And then make sure whenever the time comes, when you decide that he's met that bar, that when you fuck his brains out, you call me and let me know how incredible it was. I need to know when I gloat that I was right."

"That's two favors."

I can hear her laugh as she hangs up. The smile on my lips remains for some time after as I think about the conversation and her advice.

Over a month ago I was in a miserable relationship, toeing the line, and not really living life. Now I'm in paradise, working toward a promotion, and am attracted to a man I'd be crazy not to be attracted to.

And he's attracted back.

Own that, Sutton. *Believe it.* And let him take some distance if he needs to without thinking the worst of the situation.

I push the chair again, close my eyes as I sway in the breeze, and take this all in.

First of all, how is this my life?

Second, how did this even happen?

Do one thing for yourself.

I did and look where that got me. But now I guess I'm moving the bar on that because I'm going to do several things for myself.

My laugh floats out on the breeze, and I push a little harder on the ground so the hammock twists and rocks.

It's definitely okay to keep doing those things for me, even if it means making Callahan work a little harder to earn me.

He still wants me. *Right?* Or have I led him on for too long that he's lost interest?

I think back over the last few weeks. The laughter and sexual tension definitely outweigh the awkward silences.

Maybe Lizzy is right. Maybe he just needs a bit of space to adjust to opening up.

It has to be that.

I sit and swing, enjoying the sunshine on my face, the ocean breeze all around me, and when I finally decide to go inside, I know the answer to my question.

I don't know if Callahan will ever figure it out, but I sure as hell plan on having fun if he tries to.

CHAPTER TWENTY-SEVEN

Callahan

WITH MY HOODIE ON AND PULLED DOWN OVER MY FOREHEAD, I keep to my space in the corner of the resort's gym. The staff trainers mill around waiting for guests to come in and work out, but the last thing I need or want is them training me.

Or kissing my ass once they realize who I am.

So I stay to my corner, wiping down the bench and replacing the dumbbells to their correct location after every use. My shoulders ache and my chest muscles burn with the satisfaction of a good workout.

I pushed myself harder today than normal. Frustrated with a check-in call from Ford where my every move was questioned. Pissed off over Solomon's mention of Gia the other day. His words were a punch to the gut to remind me of the man I really am. The one who prioritized pussy over family, nameless sex over integrity, and playtime over worktime. It was a blatant reminder that Sutton doesn't need my shit. *She was right to demand more than another night of mindless fucking.*

And then there's Sutton herself. How I let my guard down the other night when that's not something I do. Ever. But there I was lying in the bed beside her letting her know about shit I've kept locked tight for years.

Shit that is no one's business, let alone a woman I'm trying to sleep with.

And yet I fucking told her a majority of it.

You'd at least think I'd get laid as a reward. I mean, a man has to have his own lines he draws, right?

But I didn't.

We didn't.

And yet, while I'm more than sexually frustrated, there must be some-thing fucking wrong with me when I say the woman can kiss. And can kiss in a way that makes every damn bone in your body want her but be satis-fied with not getting more.

This is becoming a problem.

A huge fucking problem.

And not because she's holding out, but because she's the only god-damn thing I want. Hell, I was all but propositioned last night after my meeting with a distributor and it held no appeal.

None.

I looked at the highly attractive woman with her come-fuck-me eyes and told her I don't mix business with pleasure.

The irony.

Because all I wanted to do was go back to the villa and do just that. But when I got to the villa and walked in, Sutton was sound asleep on the couch. She was sprawled out, mouth open, pajamas askew, hair a mess, and I just stood there and stared at her. Stared and wanted and wondered.

There was no regret going home to that instead of taking up the offer given by a woman whose name I can't even remember.

Sutton has broken my libido.

Goddamn broken it so that all I want is her.

How fucking fair is that?

To want a woman who I don't deserve but crave nonetheless?

It's going to be a long few weeks. Fucking torturous.

I grab a heavier dumbbell. Anything to push her out of my mind even if for a few fucking minutes.

"Have you seen the new chick?"

I glance up to see two of the staff members walk in from the back. They have stacks of towels in their hands that they must be resupplying.

"Which one?" the blond-haired guy says.

"Dark hair. Nice rack. Legs for days," the dark-haired one says.

"You need to be a little more specific than that." Blond one laughs.

"She's management, I think. Here for a couple of months to fix shit and fire people," Dark Hair says, causing me to pause mid bicep curl. *Sutton.*

She's fucking everywhere.

"We could def use some shit fixed around here, and I'd be more than happy to see a few of the annoying peeps go too." Blond guy laughs.

"She could fire me all she wants so long as she gives me a few parting gifts on the way out the door."

"I bet she's wild in the sack," Blond says. "Those reserved, prissy ones always are."

Dark Hair playfully shoves Blond and says, "I'll let you know when I'm finished with her."

I drop the weight with a thud on the mat, both employees glance in my direction, but keep talking about things they want to do to Sutton.

My blood boils.

I pull my hood off my head and walk toward them. Dark Hair sees me first and the next crass comment on his tongue dies when my eyes meet his, and I give him the best *fuck you* smile I can muster through my fury.

"Can I help you?" he asks as Blond turns around and sucks in a startled breath.

So he was the one who paid attention at the company-wide meeting we had the other day.

"Gentlemen." I meet both of their eyes and don't miss the nudge Blond gives Dark Hair.

"Mr. Sharpe. Hi. We—we were just—"

"Saying things you shouldn't be saying in front of your boss, let alone guests here who are trying to enjoy their vacation. It's unprofessional, don't you think?" I cross my arms over my chest to prevent me from reaching out and wringing both of their necks.

"We weren't—You misheard—"

"No. I didn't. I'm well aware of what I heard."

"I'm sorry, but you know how it is when guys talk," Dark Hair says, trying to act like because we're both men, I'll be fine with him bragging about wanting to fuck Sutton.

Not on his life.

"When guys talk, hmm?" I ask and angle my head to the side to freeze him into wishing he hadn't just said those words. "Is that what this was? Two guys talking about how they'd like to fuck their superior?" I lift a brow. "Sounds to me like two guys about to get fired."

"Fuck," Dark Hair groans like the immature prick I'm certain he is.

"Seriously?" Blond asks.

I look from one to the other and back, remembering how many times Ford and Ledge and I would talk like this—still do at times—but for some reason this time it hits me differently.

"Not that it's any of your business, but she's already associated with someone much higher on the pay scale than you. Furthermore, conversations about how exactly you want to *tap her*—or any other woman for that matter—especially on company time, will result in dismissal. Have I made myself clear?"

I stride out the doors without looking back because I'm proud of myself for showing restraint I don't believe those two little fuckers deserve.

Talking like that about Sutton. Fucking hell.

It's like after the other night, I feel this strange sense of protection over her now. I'm not sure why or how or what the hell is wrong with me, but I do.

And I fucking hate it.

I don't even know who I am right now.

You're just occupying your time, Callahan.

You were being a decent human standing up for another human because maybe, after all the shit that's gone on, you feel the need to.

You're bending, Cal, not begging.

I don't like any of this. Not one bit.

Not that it's any of your business, but she's already associated with someone much higher on the pay scale than you.

Good God.

I wander down a path to the beach and then back toward the villas and then back toward the office, suddenly uncertain about everything when I'm not an uncertain guy. *Ever.*

My every instinct says to pack my shit up and go. To walk the fuck away and go back to being a nomad like I was for the six months after my father's passing. There was freedom to it. Simplicity.

And now everything just feels complicated.

"Fuck," I bark out to no one in particular.

I can't go.

I have to stay and finish what I set out to do to honor my dad. Who am I if I can't at least do that for the man who gave me everything?

Fucking emotions.

The ones I feel that are unresolved over my father's death and the ones that being around Sutton have drummed up.

I should go to the office and work. Run over the latest cost estimates that came in this afternoon to see if any of this nonstop dinner-meeting-bullshit is even worth it.

Restless, I head in that direction, but when I get there and see all the lights off, the thought of the solitude I normally love doesn't sound so appealing.

You're all screwed up, Sharpe. Since when do you not love your solitude?

I know the answer, but don't want to admit it to myself.

Ever since I've shared the space with Sutton. The quiet humming in her bedroom to whatever music is on her earbuds. The soft clatter of dishes in the sink late at night. The muted sound of the television as she laughs at something on the rare occasion she watches it.

This is fucking stupid. How are you used to something you don't actively participate in, Cal? Huh?

Keone.

He's the answer. I'll visit him, indulge in his quick wit. He'll keep serving me drink after drink until all this fucking noise in my head abates, and I can think straight again.

With a sigh, I turn a corner on the path toward the bar and run into Sutton. We both make garbled yelps. But it's only when she steps back that I notice the skirt that's too short and a shirt that's too tight and, fuck, I love everything about it.

So much for steering clear of her.

"And you're going where?" I ask.

"To item number eight on my top-ten list." Her smile is quick and disarming.

"What is number eight?"

The smile crawls over her lips. "Singles night at Isla del Mar."

Like *that?* Over my dead body.

"I'm pretty sure I told you that you weren't going."

"And I'm pretty sure I told you that no one tells me what to do." She shrugs unapologetically while I hear the trainers' comments from the gym earlier today. "Besides, you've been avoiding me for some reason or another.

Gia says hi," she mimics Solomon in a way that completely throws me off guard. "What do you care if I go dance and have fun?"

"You're jealous?"

"I am not. You're just being a jerk."

"You're not going, Sutton."

She takes a step forward, her eyes darting around while the darkness plays shadows over her face. Her voice is low when she speaks. "The whole dominant thing? That only works with me in the bedroom." She pokes me in the chest and I chuckle, her determination and temper totally sexy. "And since it's clear we're not there nor will we be anytime soon, then it seems you can't exactly tell me what I can and cannot do."

There's that moxie of hers I love. Christ, it gets me hard.

"I'm your boss."

"Correction. I'm your consultant. We work for each other, *with* each other, and—"

"You're so full of shit."

"Excuse me?"

"The whole boss, employee, we can't sleep together theory. You just said it yourself. That we work *with* each other, not you *for* me. So if that doesn't hold water, then perhaps the *what do I get out of this* doesn't hold any either." I cross my arms over my chest and smile slowly. "Seems to me you just like playing hard to get."

"And it seems to me you haven't figured out the answer to the question."

I want to kiss her. I want to pull her to me by the back of the neck and taste those lips of hers. But the guests and staff milling about in my periphery tell me I can't.

Her eyes hold mine and the look in them says she knows exactly what I'm thinking.

"You're not going. How's that for an answer?"

"Why not? Because you know what you think when you walk into a club? The things you want to do to the woman you set your sights on and the end result you're aiming for?" She lifts her eyebrows and chuckles. "I'm off the clock, Sharpe. And when I'm off the clock, you don't get to say what I can or can't do."

Motherfucker.

She's going anyway. She's going and every man in that place is going to want what I can't have.

Can I hope she kept at least one pair of granny panties and she's chosen to wear them tonight? Can I at least have that?

But one more look at her tiny, tight skirt and I know there is no way in hell she has them on.

Christ. At this moment, I'm just praying she came to her senses and has something on underneath.

"You're wondering, aren't you?" she asks with a smirk, her gaze following mine, which clearly isn't hiding my thoughts.

"I gave them back to you."

"You did. I'll grant you that, but I also told you I wasn't going to wear them simply to drive you crazy."

"Sutton," I growl, my jaw clenched in frustration.

"Do I, or don't I? That's the big question."

"This isn't funny." I reach out to touch her and she takes a step back, one eyebrow quirked and her eyes darting around to see if anyone is paying attention.

"This thing you're feeling? It's called sexual frustration, Callahan. It manifests itself in sudden outbursts or claims over a person when you have no right making them." She steps into me and whispers, "It's also hot as fucking hell. See you later."

She holds her hand up and wiggles her fingers in a wave as she starts to walk away.

"A date."

Why didn't I think of that sooner?

"What?" She looks over her shoulder.

"A date. That's the answer, right? You want the wine and dine before the sixty-nine part?"

"That never hurts—making the woman feel like more than just your *fuck toy* is always a good thing, but sorry, it's not the answer. You might need to take care of that inside." She motions to my semi pressing against the seam of my pants. "Don't wait up."

And then she turns on her heel and walks into the darkness.

Oh yeah, she's definitely playing with fire.

197

CHAPTER TWENTY-EIGHT

Sutton

CLUBS HAVE NEVER BEEN MY SCENE.

Sure, I went with Lizzy that fated night because I just needed to feel alive—and boy did *he* make me feel alive. And now, if I'm honest with myself, I'm here because the last thing I'm going to do is let Callahan tell me what I can and can't do. Not after he's been ignoring me—which *hello?* Why is he? Because we actually talked? Because our kissing felt way more intimate than anything we've done before?

And especially not after him pulling the Neanderthal role earlier.

That, and I have a feeling he'll show up here too.

A man as possessive and demanding as he is won't be thrilled that I'm here alone. Especially not when *he* was what happened to me the last time I was in the same position.

I bet he's pacing back and forth at the villa.

Or standing in the shadows watching me right now.

My money's on the latter.

Guess I better dance my ass off to let him know I'm not waiting around for him to come to his senses.

Truth be told, I'd rather be back at the villa relaxing. It's been a long week of overthinking and frankly, I'm exhausted.

However, it really is pertinent to see what the competition is doing so I can make ours even better.

And I have in fact, done just that. Mental notes have been made and my phone already has a dozen pictures or so of unique touches I'd like to have a designer look at and then take a few steps further for the Ocean's Edge's club.

Our venue is significantly nicer as a whole, so the transition and upgrades shouldn't be too complicated or costly.

I take a sip of my second drink and awkwardly look around. It's weird to be in a club by yourself and not have a group of girlfriends to hang with or have fun with. To even have the confidence to pull it off.

And honestly, I don't have the confidence right now. It's one thing to have it when I'm one on one with Callahan—there's something about him that makes me feel empowered. Confident. I hate even admitting that to myself because I'm coming off a situation where I let a man have power over my emotions. Never again.

And yet, the power Callahan gives me is completely different in the best of ways.

"You might as well have a good time instead of standing here like a wallflower sipping that drink of yours, Sutton."

"Brady! You were able to make it!" Relief floods through me to have a friend here.

"I couldn't let you brave these shark-infested waters alone. I mean, unless you want to, of course."

"No. Thank you. God, I was just feeling like such a loser standing here by myself."

"Not anymore." He taps his drink against mine and offers a devilish grin. "I brought reinforcements with me." He turns and motions to some familiar faces. "I figured who better to invite along than the staff who might be working this revamped club?"

"That's great. Awesome," I shout above the music. *Why didn't I think of that?*

Because I was too busy thinking about Callahan and wondering what the hell is going on with him.

"I figured it might help for the staff to see you here, hands-on and trying, instead of thinking of you as the corporate witch who feels threatening."

"Threatening? I'm here to help them."

"You know that. I know that. But change is scary to a lot of people and so far, with the new ownership, not much has happened. So you being here and them being here might make you appear a bit more human to them."

I grab Brady's forearm and squeeze. "Thank you. Truly. That means a lot."

"Of course. Now, let's have another drink and dance."

And dance we do. Until we're hot and sweaty and stumbling off the dance floor because we need air and space from all the people that are packed together.

"I'll get drinks," Brady says. "You go to the bathroom, and I'll meet you back here."

"Sounds like a plan."

A smile is plastered to my face as I make my way through the crowd. This place is insane. Full of more pretty people than should be legal to have all in one place. But there is no VIP area, no special place to strive to get into.

This is definitely on the list of things to fight for—to negotiate over—for Ocean's Edge.

An added bonus is this was just what the doctor ordered after the week I had. To let loose with Brady and other staff and forget about everything for a while.

I'm almost to the restroom when someone grabs my arm and pulls me into an open hallway. My yelp is overshadowed by the low bass throbbing through the speakers as I land solidly against a male chest.

"Callahan." I giggle and try to steady myself, the alcohol swimming in my veins.

"Drunk?" he asks, his lips so close to my mouth, I stare at it. Want it. Am desperate for it.

"*Happy*. What are you doing here?"

"Reminding you of everything you still want but are denying yourself."

And with that being his only warning, he slants his lips over mine. Brands mine. *Brands me*. The kiss is laden with hunger and desperation that has my knees nearly buckling. His tongue clashes with mine and makes my head dizzy. I fist his shirt as he cups my breast and squeezes.

My moan is swallowed by the kiss and the music as my body begs for the feel of his against me. On me. In me.

His hand is in my ponytail like that first night, when he fists it and drags his mouth from mine to come up for air.

"And I'm reminding myself why the fucking confusion is worth it," he mutters as our gazes lock.

"Callahan." I don't know if I'm warning him off or begging him to stay in that one single utterance of his name.

But one thing is clear—the doubt I felt over the past few days is gone. *He still wants me.*

"Let me get you out of here," he says.

"That would be a mistake."

"Wouldn't be the first one I've made." He offers an arrogant smile that causes that flip-flop in my stomach again.

"No. I mean . . . Brady is here and—"

He looks out to the crowd beyond and then gives a quick shake of his head before saying, "Ours will be even better." He presses one last kiss to my lips and says, "Go back to your friends then," before striding away quickly.

"Callahan." His name is a strangled cry this time. "*Please. Stay.*" But my words are drowned out by the music, and with his absence, I'm suddenly left feeling lonely. *Empty.*

That has to be the alcohol talking.

Do I chase after him? Do I run after him and—

"Sutton. There you are," Brady says as he grabs my arm and puts a drink in my hand. "I thought I lost you."

"No. Sorry. I was . . ."

"Who was that?" He looks in the direction Callahan just took off in. "A hot hookup for later, I hope."

"Who was who?" I ask and gulp down the drink. "Oh. That guy." I wave in the same direction Brady is looking. "He bumped into me and I spilled his drink. That's all. Nothing more."

Lies.

All lies. I wanted to keep kissing him. I want to go back to the villa and do more.

But I can't. I won't.

I'm definitely going to need more drinks to help with that.

CHAPTER TWENTY-NINE

Callahan

WALKING AWAY AT THE CLUB WAS HARD.
Wanting her is even harder.
And this back and forth is hardest on my balls—who are feeling the brunt of this game.

But I held my ground. I didn't push her against the wall and take and taint her like I wanted to right there in the club. There's something to be said for that because restraint isn't my strong suit.

That's what she wants, isn't it? For me to prove I have no control? That I only think of my needs and not hers or the possible repercussions and fallout that would harm her?

So I did the unthinkable, something the me of last week would have never done—*I walked the fuck away.*

And now as the clock keeps ticking later and later, I'm sitting in our darkened villa questioning my choices.

Next time, I won't.

Next time, I'll say *fuck the bullshit game* and take exactly what I want because this, her, us, is driving me fucking insane.

So I take another sip of my whiskey, waiting with my eyes closed and my head swimming and my thoughts running.

Two in the morning. That's when I hear the fumbling at the front door and the laughed-out curse as the lock beeps to tell her that her key card didn't engage.

Then the door pushes open and Sutton stumbles inside with a "Whoopsie," falling from her mouth. She drops her purse on the counter with a loud thud and then clumsily pulls her shoes off one by one before tossing them haphazardly to the floor.

She giggles again—that's twice tonight she's giggled. It's so strange to hear the sound from such a controlled, headstrong woman, but it pulls a smile to my lips. She weaves over to pick up a water bottle from the table and takes a long, greedy gulp before simply standing there with her eyes closed and a dopey smile on her lips.

Her skirt is crooked and her top is falling off one shoulder. She looks like a hot mess and yet, still adorable when before, I've only seen her as sexy.

Stop, Callahan. Let her go to bed and not know you're sitting here.

I can't resist.

"Have fun?"

She jumps at the sound of my voice and then visibly relaxes when she finds me sitting across the room from her in the dark. "You waited up for me?" She moves across the room. "How cute."

"Just unwinding," I murmur, angling my head to look up at her where she stands in front of me.

"In the dark at whatever time this is?"

"Mm-hmm. I like this time of night when everyone is asleep and the silence speaks."

"I thought you were a morning person."

"I'm a lot of things, Sutton."

She stares at me, head tilted, teeth biting her bottom lip. *Fuck, she's cute.* "What does the silence say?" she whispers as she takes it upon herself to step between my legs and sit on one of my knees. I put one hand on her waist to help steady her. Her glassy eyes meet mine and she narrows them while she waits for an answer.

"That you're going to have one hell of a headache in the morning." I move my hand off her waist and play with a lock of hair that's fallen out of her ponytail, rubbing it between my fingers.

"Maybe. Maybe not." She yawns and looks at me with half-closed eyelids. "Do I have an expiration date, Johnnie?"

"A what?" I laugh.

"Brady told me you're the type of man who gives a woman an expiration date—that you only play with them for so long—so I was wondering if I have one?" The look in her eyes is so earnest it undoes me in a way I've never been undone before.

Is this her way of asking if I'm over her?

Does she not see that that's the furthest thing from the truth?

"Sutton—"

"I'm sleepy," she murmurs and then without any warning, leans forward and lays on my chest. Her body snuggles into mine with her cheek on my shoulder and the tip of her nose under my jaw.

I hesitate. I'm not sure why I do after we slept together in her bed the other night, but I do.

I take that back.

I know why I hesitate. It's because since that night, things have changed between us and maybe I'm just desperate to get us back to before. To when I didn't snuggle or care. Back to when I had sex then parted ways. Back to when there was no meaningful conversation or room for misunderstanding that *more* might be an option.

Back to when I thought I was a good thing for her but now fear I'm not.

And yet . . . I wrap my arm around her, pull her into me, and breathe her in.

"Did you figure it out yet, Cal?" She emits a slurred chuckle. "Do you mind if I call you Cal?"

"Yes. I mind. My brothers call me that, and it's only when they're trying to piss me off." I run a hand down her back as I think about it. "Lately they seem to call me that all the time."

"Hmm," she says and then falls quiet. I think she's actually fallen asleep on me, but then she finally speaks, her voice soft. "I know how that feels. The always being in trouble part." She chuckles softly. "He was never happy with what I did. He set me up to fail for his own amusement. Asked me questions in front of his friends only to let me know my answers were wrong. Encouraged me to take the painting class I'd been wanting to take, only to make fun of what I created at the class showing. I thought love meant giving him what he needed, but . . . he took parts of me I didn't even realize I'd given away until it was too late."

"Sutton," I say, uncertain if I'm giving it as a warning to make her aware of how much she's sharing when she's tipsy, or so I feel better that I did while wanting her to continue regardless.

"His career came first. His happiness. His . . . *pleasure*." She snorts. "That's why I'm here. That's why Lizzy told me to do one thing for me." *Lizzy? One thing?* "What girl turns down promotions because her boyfriend's ego gets hurt that she might advance faster than he does? This girl, right here." She lifts a hand and then lets it fall with a thud against my chest. "What girl is so ashamed that she let him steal days and years and hours from her life when she thought she was strong but really wasn't? This girl, right here."

"You are strong, Collins," I murmur and press a kiss to her head as an unexplained fury vibrates beneath my skin.

She laughs as if she doesn't believe a word I've said. "That's what you think." Another snort. She runs the tip of her nose against my jawbone and then back down. "Don't be too sexy. Don't draw too much attention to yourself. Talking to other men is considered flirting to me," she says in a pretend man's voice. "And God forbid any of that was allowed regardless of how alive it made me feel inside." She shakes her head. "*All I wanted was to feel alive.*"

"He's gone now," I whisper.

"*Clint.* Clint was his name." She lifts a middle finger in the air that makes me smile.

"I've never liked that name."

"Me neither."

"Fuck you, Clint." I lift my glass in a silent toast and take a drink.

She laughs now, her hand sliding between the buttons on my shirt and resting on the bare skin of my chest. Does she have any clue how much I crave her touch?

"*You* make me feel alive, Callahan."

"Sutton . . ." This woman leaves me at a loss for words more than anyone else in my life.

"Did you know that this girl had no clue you could have multiple orgasms during sex because her boyfriend was selfish and didn't give a rat's ass about her pleasure? I didn't know until . . . *you*."

Something akin to emotion lodges in my throat and makes it hard to swallow. The urge to lift her chin and kiss her mouth is there. The want to slide my hand up the line of her thigh and dip into the heaven between them even stronger.

But right now, nothing feels right. Not her confession. Not how it makes me feel. Not that I'm okay with a woman basically lying on top of me without the promise for more.

"Why can't you be what I need?" she murmurs sleepily, absently, as if she's already dreaming.

"I'm not what anyone needs, Collins," I whisper. *You have to be worth something to be needed.* "Ever."

"I disagree," she says in a childish voice. "Why haven't you tried to sleep with me again? Is it because my expiration date has past? Is it because you've moved on?"

"It's none of that," I murmur, hearing my own answer and feeling uncertain about what it means.

"Then fuck me, Johnnie," she whispers. The same words she whispered that first night, and every ounce of my being has to fight the urge not to respond.

"Not like this, Collins." I press another absent kiss to the top of her hair. "Not when you're like this."

"Why?"

Because I want you to remember. Because I want to know every fucking sensation is being felt by you too.

"Because you deserve better than that."

"Such a good man. You know that, don't you? What a good man you are? That's why I've fallen for you." She emits a soft chuckle that falls off and her breath evens out.

I swear I stop breathing for a second. She's drunk. It's the alcohol talking, and I'm just being a nice guy so she's mistaking that feeling of comfort for more.

You can explain it away any which way you want, Callahan, but those words just slipped past her lips. Words that come on the heels of so much more blatant honesty that it's pretty damn hard to ignore them.

Hell, if my pulse isn't racing right now, and my mouth isn't suddenly dry.

"Thank you, Callahan." Her words slur as she presses a soft kiss to the side of my neck. "For making me realize to never settle again."

I open my mouth to speak, but fuck. Emotions, thoughts, bullshit thunder through me in a confusing eddy that leave me speechless. And as I struggle with what to say, a soft snore slips from her mouth and saves me the trouble.

It's hard to brush it under the rug in true Sharpe fashion when her warm body is still lying on top of me and her words are front and center.

For making me realize to never settle again.

Sutton Pierce.

That's why I've fallen for you.

She talks like she's this weak woman, but all I've seen from her is strength. Talk about the queen of contradictions. Sexy and defiant but a little bit broken underneath.

Aren't we all, Cal? Aren't you?

My sigh is heavy because the answer is yes, but mine is self-inflicted and hers was at the hand of another.

So is that what this is all about? This game? The need to know another man isn't going to screw her over before she gives more of herself?

Christ. Is that what I do? Screw women over and make them feel like the slimy fucker Clint did? I scrub a hand over my face and then rest it on her bare thigh that's draped over mine.

No. No fucking way. I don't promise shit—more, forever, happily ever after—anything of the sort. I don't demean. I don't belittle. I give pleasure. *I walk away.*

And yet, her words make me question my actions when I've never questioned them before.

What's in it for me?

Is this her way to get some of the pieces back? The ones he stole and ruined? To own who she is and the sexuality he shamed her for?

Is that the answer to her question?

What's in it for me?

Is the answer *her?* That she finds herself again?

I chew the inside of my cheek and listen to the silence scream.

To my thoughts whispering quietly inside that scream.

And I know I don't want that to be the right answer.

That it can't be.

Because I'm pretty certain that once Sutton Pierce finds herself, she'll be gone to me.

She'll know her worth, she'll own it, and she'll know without a doubt that a guy like me, who doesn't make promises, isn't worth her salt.

She wants . . . *deserves* a man who stays. Who knows how to commit with his whole heart. *And that man is not me.* I can't let Sutton think that I'm up for her challenge.

The game has changed.

And this selfish prick doesn't want to play anymore.

CHAPTER THIRTY

Callahan

Eleven Months Ago

THE SAILBOAT ROCKS GENTLY BACK AND FORTH AS I STARE out at the horizon, miles upon miles of blue water before us.

I could say the briny scent in my nose and the sun on my face is enough to wash away the bullshit from earlier—but it'd be a lie.

A total fucking lie.

"Where's Dad?" I ask as I walk into the conference room to find Ford sitting in a chair and Ledger standing with his back against the glass and his arms crossed over his chest.

Fuck. They know.

"Dad is irrelevant at this point," Ledger grits out, steel in his jaw and ice in his voice.

"It's his company and therefore he should be here for—"

"For what?" Ledger asks, voice rising with each syllable. "He can't protect you from this, Cal."

"What are you talking about?" I ask.

"Don't play the bullshit innocent routine. Sharpe International is the fucking laughing stock right now because you signed a deal to buy a resort so you could fuck the owner's daughter."

What the fuck?

"Everybody knows, Cal. Thanks to your bathroom proposition, you selling us out to get some prized pussy is the talk of the fucking town."

I glance over to my father. He has a soft smile on his lips, a glass of scotch in his hand, and I wonder if I were able to see his eyes behind his sunglasses, what they would tell me. Is he present? Has his mind escaped him again? Does he even remember what happened earlier today?

For his sake, I hope he doesn't.

"I didn't sleep with her," I say, meeting both of their eyes.

"Jesus fucking Christ," Ledger bellows. "Don't forget that we know you."

"Dad can explain everything. He wants the resort as a tribute to Mom. It was his promise to her to buy a piece of land there one day. How—"

"And last night he told me he'd spent his entire thirties in Ibiza. We all know that's not true because he was here raising us," Ledger says, his eyes narrowed and mistrusting.

"He should be here," I shout, hand slapping against the table. I refuse to believe he didn't have a moment of clarity. I refuse to believe that the one moment of lucidity was the disease fucking tricking me once again. I refuse to accept that I believed it.

"He's at home, Callahan," Ford says. "He's being relieved of his active duties in the company."

"What?" I practically scream, my tongue suddenly thick in my mouth.

"It's best for everyone right now," Ledger says softly.

Panic shudders through me. "That will kill him. Not being here. Not being a part of the company and—"

"So which is it, Cal?" Ledger pushes off the wall and walks toward me. "The signing of the deal. Because if it was Dad's doing, he's more harm to us than good right now, but if it was your doing . . . then he can stay at the helm a little longer."

"You okay, Callahan?" my dad asks, pulling my attention to the here and now instead of thoughts of earlier.

"Yes. Just a lot on my mind." I glance over my shoulder to where the captain says something to a crew member about the jib, and then back to my dad.

"Your brothers will get over it. They always do."

I nod, draw in a deep breath, and lie. "I'm sure they will."

"We're Sharpes." He chuckles. "We fight hard, but we love deeper."

"I know, Dad." I reach out and pat his hand. "I know."

"Do you see that spot over there?" he asks me, raising his hand with his glass in it toward the shores of Long Island.

"What about it?" His brows furrow behind his glasses, and I can visibly see the confusion take over his expression. "Dad?"

"Just beyond the reef, there."

I glance at my dad and then back to the shoreline that clearly doesn't have a reef—we're nowhere near one. I struggle with whether to tell him that or let him keep talking. The last thing I want to do is upset him when he's in the one place he loves more than the office.

"Yes, I see it," I lie.

"Maybe one day you'll fall in love and bring her to this place too, Callahan. Your mother would love that."

I offer a reassuring smile and then shake my head. "I can't imagine that happening any time soon, Dad." There are too many places I still want to go. Things to do. Anything other than being in that office for hours on end. "Especially when I'm stuck in the office—"

"You're not stuck there. You have the privilege of being there." His sigh is soft and content. "The only days I feel like myself are when I'm sitting in that office, seeing all I've built. Other days, I can't remember a thing. But that office, that place, you boys, keep me sane."

That place keeps him sane.

And that right there? That's why I just nodded as Ledger and Ford got years of resentment out in our fight earlier. That's why I took the blame over the deal so that my father could still sit at the helm and hold on to whatever scraps of sanity he has left.

I've done a lot of wrong that he's forgiven me for.

It's the least I can do now to make sure he gets to hold tight a little longer to his joy, even if it means enduring disapproval from my brothers.

Even if we never recover.

"You're right, Dad. It is a privilege." I blink the tears away that well in my eyes, needing to hold on to this moment with him despite his mind clearly being in a different place. "Tell me more about your time here with Mom."

CHAPTER THIRTY-ONE

Sutton

I MAY OR MAY NOT HAVE A HANGOVER THAT HAS LASTED LONGER THAN any I've had in some time. While I'm more than grateful for the Advil and water Callahan left on my nightstand for when I woke up, it didn't do much to lessen the pounding in my head.

And maybe I'm nursing my symptoms more than I normally would by staying and working at the villa instead of the office because I'm too afraid to face Callahan after the things I said last night. While my memory may be fuzzy, I'm pretty sure I slung some words around that probably shouldn't have been slung around.

If he wanted distance over talking about families and pasts and kissing, then he sure as hell is probably going to be moving out today—if he hasn't already—to get as far away from me as possible.

I groan and press my fingers to my eyes.

I have to fix this.

I have to talk to him and let him know that it was the alcohol talking. That I'm a sappy, cheerful drunk. Maybe he'll accept it for what it's worth, and hopefully we can go back to whatever it is that we are.

Hopefully.

We just need to have sex and get it over with. Maybe that will help shift the focus back to that? Maybe if we both give in to the physical, we can . . . somehow get back to the us I probably screwed up last night.

Hiding here in the villa isn't going to do any of that.

I'm dressed and heading out the door to find Callahan when I get a text from Brady to meet him at The Cove. That my presence is being requested.

When my texts remain unanswered after some time, I decide to head out to find him.

The resort is buzzing with activity this evening. Tonight is our second Beachfront Friday and guests are milling about on their way to see what all the preparations and signage are about.

It brings a smile to my face to see a difference already from my first day here to what I think is now my forty-somethingth. It seems that guests are preferring to stay at the resort and enjoy its activities rather than head to other resorts.

We still have a long way to go, but the new resort signage definitely has set the tone for things to come and improvements to expect. New uniforms for the staff have been ordered, which only add to the sophisticated esthetic that Sharpe properties exude.

And Callahan's dinner meetings have paid off. We've had a ten percent cost reduction from our linen supplier as well as a twelve percent cut from our alcohol vendor. Add to that, he's found a more professional landscaping company who will actually do more for less. *In other words, Ocean's Edge was being swindled.*

Things are definitely heading in the right direction.

And that's exactly what I told Roz earlier when we talked on the phone. Despite the steady drumbeat pounding in my head, I was able to update her on the week's progress. I could all but see her checking off items on her work-in-progress status sheets she keeps for each project.

"This is how success starts, Sutton," she'd said before hanging up.

And she's right. This is how success starts.

One building brick upon another.

And after Callahan told me about the origins of the resort's purchase and the negative projections by his brothers, I'm further determined to turn this place around. Not only for myself but so he can prove to them he's capable of doing his job.

Plus, I'm not going to lie. It's exciting to see changes happening so fast.

Maybe his brothers will step back and praise him for following through with what he said he would.

But the idea of him walking away from all of this when it's done makes my chest hurt. To have a family dynamic that seems repairable and not want to work at it kills me.

Then again, I may not know the full story.

I wander over by the bar and smile when I see Keone. That man is a fount of knowledge when it comes to the staff, to the island, and to the whispers no one is supposed to hear. I seriously wish we could duplicate him.

"Hey, Keone. How's the night shaping up?"

"All good here, Ms. Sutton. This new Beachfront Friday thing you've got going is definitely good for business."

"Good to hear."

"And you? You good? Can I get you a drink?"

I cringe at the thought of a drink. Screw the hair of the dog theory. "I'm good. Thanks though. I'm on my way to meet Brady at The Cove, but I was just trying to find Callahan before I do."

"The man is in high demand tonight, that's for sure." He laughs, pulling me from the text that just hit my phone from Brady telling me he figured out whatever it was he needed me for.

"High demand? Does he have more meetings?"

Keone shakes his head, and then lifts his chin behind me. I follow his stare.

Wow. The woman standing there is stunning and yet, at the same time, seems out of place. Sure, she has the look of a Sharpe International regular—commanding attention and acting as if she owns the place—but something about her has me straightening my shoulders.

"Keone? Who is—"

"Gia Diamante," he says. "She was just looking for Callahan too. My guess is she's not looking for a 'meeting' though."

His chuckle resonates as my stomach drops.

That's Gia?

The same Gia that Solomon said was keen to see Callahan again?

I take a step back and offer a muddled goodbye to Keone, desperate to get out of here before he sees what I'm sure is all over my face. *Jealousy.*

Is that why I couldn't find Callahan? Is he meeting up with Gia tonight?

"You okay, Ms. Sutton? You want me to tell Mr. Sharpe that you were asking for him?"

Hell. No.

219

"No. I'm good. I'll catch him tomorrow."

And then I'm gone, feeling sick and needy and angry. When Callahan runs, he sure runs fast.

I need to talk to him. *For what it's worth.* I need to figure out what this is or isn't so I can either get completely on or off the roller coaster.

With that thought in mind, I rush toward our offices but the light is off in his window.

It's only when I'm walking back toward The Cove that I finally spot him. *Callahan.* He's standing near the entrance to the restaurant, hands shoved in his pockets, and back toward me.

My chest constricts at the sight of him, his broad shoulders and tall silhouette placed against the setting sun.

If I ever wondered if this whole thing between us had an expiration date, the sight of Gia there and him here, presumably waiting for her, just reinforced the notion.

What do I do?

How do I handle this?

Do I let him know I still want him?

Do I let him go now and save myself the hurt before I get in deeper?

Just say *something*, Sutton. *Anything.*

"There you are," I finally manage as I take a few steps closer to him. Keep it simple. Nonchalant. Professional. "I wanted to thank you for the . . ." *Advil you left on my nightstand.* But the words don't come, because Ledger was right that first time I met them. *The longer you know us, the easier it will be to tell us apart.* "Ledger? Or is it Ford?" I ask, startled and a little surprised to see him here. And knowing I almost just indicated how close Callahan and I are.

His smile spreads into a wide smile. "You're very observant, Ms. Pierce. And it's Ledger. Great to see you again."

"It's Sutton. Please. And we're glad to have you so . . . unexpectedly."

"Nice recovery." His laugh is rich, and I have to take a step back to remind myself that this is Ledger, and not Callahan. "But I come in peace." He holds his hands up. "Just wanted to see what's going on here and get a look at where all our money is going."

I hear those words with a different tinge now but keep my welcoming smile. "Will you be staying with us long?"

"Just for the night and through the morning."

"A quick trip then?" And I'm uncertain why I breathe a sigh of relief because of it. Almost as if I want him gone so that he and Callahan don't come to blows.

"Yes. I have business to tend to in Texas so I figured this wouldn't be a bad layover spot for the night."

A little out of the way, but . . .

"Not at all." I hold my hands out to motion to the beauty all around us. "Then I won't be keeping you. I'm sure you have lots to discuss with your brother while you're here."

"Actually, it was you I was going to seek out. That's why I asked Brady to summon you here for me." His smile is warm, his amber eyes inviting.

"Oh. Sure. Yes." Brady knew he was here and didn't warn me? *Thanks a lot.* "What can I do for you?"

"I'd like to go over some of the changes and hear your take on everything. Do you have plans for dinner? The Cove has made room so they can fit us in."

"Of course. I'm not exactly dressed for dinner. I can run back and change."

"Sutton. Please." He holds up his hands and laughs. "I have no agenda. I swear. There is no need to be on edge because I'm here."

"I'm not nervous, I just wasn't expecting you and wouldn't want to make the wrong impression with my island casual attire."

"Your island casual is just fine. I assure you." He looks around as if he's getting a lay of the land—or looking for his brother—before he holds his hand out for me to lead the way inside. "I look forward to hearing about everything."

My heart thumps in my chest as we walk down the path.

I'm not sure why I'm so rattled about him being here.

This is his resort just as much as it's Callahan's.

But I haven't slept with Ledger.

And I fear that, somehow, I'll give it away that I have with his brother. *Who may or may not be meeting up with another woman tonight.*

CHAPTER THIRTY-TWO

Callahan

"WELL, WELL, WELL, IF IT ISN'T THE ELUSIVE CALLAHAN Sharpe in the flesh."

Every part of me stills at the voice, rejects the sound of it. Keone's eyebrows raise before I slowly turn around and face the woman standing behind me.

"Gia."

"You remembered my name. Too bad you didn't remember my hotel room number." Her painted red lips curve up in a seductive smile as her eyes drink me in.

"Some things are better left forgotten." I manage a not so friendly smile.

"*Everybody knows, Cal. Thanks to your bathroom proposition, you selling us out to get some prized pussy is the talk of the fucking town.*"

Gia would love knowing her actions caused a major showdown between the Sharpe brothers. *Something we've yet to recover from.* She'd revel in it.

"Now, you're just being mean." She pouts dramatically, knowing that every single person's eyes in this bar are on the stunning woman before me.

A woman I have zero interest in.

"So you've sought me out, what exactly is it that you need from me, Gia?"

Her low chuckle vibrates through me. "Now that's a loaded question if ever I've heard one."

I offer a smile that I'm certain doesn't reach my eyes. "If you're here for what I think you're here for, I'm not interested."

"We have unfinished . . . matters, though."

"Actually, we don't." I stare at this woman who I would have given anything before to fuck. *Anything.* And I look at her now and find her attractive physically but nothing more.

"Callahan. We both know that's not true," she purrs and runs a fingertip over the edge of my shoulder.

I shrug away from her touch and stand from my seat. "Doesn't this game ever get old?"

"What game is that?" And that's when I see the truth. Sutton isn't playing a game at all. Never has. *She genuinely expects more for herself. As she ought to.* Whereas Gia . . .

"The rich playgirl routine where you show up, cause a scene, and then expect to get fucked?"

Her smile returns despite the insult. "I wouldn't throw stones in glass houses, Callahan." She leans in and whispers, "Once upon a time those words used to define you too."

Tou-fucking-ché.

I stare at her, jaw clenched as I absorb her words. There is truth in them I don't want to face but can't deny.

When Solomon mentioned her, I knew she'd seek me out. Knew she'd show up to see me and try to rectify that blow I gave to her ego. A woman like her has never been told no.

I should know. I never had either . . . before Sutton.

I look at Gia and see everything I used to want.

What's in it for me? If Gia uttered those words, I'd consider her a manipulative bitch.

But Sutton deserves to ask that question.

She also has no reason to be jealous of Gia, and I need her to know that. I need to find her. Because when I think of Sutton, I see everything I think I need.

Jesus.

When did that happen?

When did that fucking happen?

"What do you want, Gia?" I ask, done with this conversation before it even starts.

"You." No hesitation. No shame.

I purse my lips and give a slight nod. "Sorry. I'm taken."

And with that, I glance at Keone, whose eyes are bigger than saucers, no doubt thinking I'm a fool for passing up the woman in front of me.

I'm heading toward the villa. My restlessness that led me to the bar now knows only one place it wants to be.

I need to find Sutton. We need to talk, and I need to know if all that she said last night wasn't just the alcohol talking but was the truth.

In particular the last part.

And then I need to figure out how the fuck I feel about it.

"Callahan. What—" Brady looks over his shoulder and then back at me with confusion owning every single damn part of him. "I mean— how?" He shakes his head.

"What?" I ask impatiently.

"I just saw you eating dinner with Sutton. How did you . . ."

"Where?" I demand, already knowing the answer.

"The Cove."

I jog toward the restaurant, not sure why I feel so panicked over the fact that Ledger or Ford or both are here.

But I do.

And I am.

Ledger.

Jealousy I've never felt before streaks through me when I look across the restaurant and see them sitting at a window seat, laughing over a glass of wine.

The sight of them together fucking consumes me. My fists clench and anger riots. All thoughts of walking up and taking a seat at the table with them dissipate.

My brother knows me better than anyone. One fucking look at me and he'll know that Sutton and I have a thing. He'll know, and in an instant, Sutton's integrity, her knowledge, her place here will be questioned. Because if she thinks I'm good, then he'll automatically think ill of her decision-making and moral compass.

Fuck.

Fuck!

I move toward the back of the restaurant, not wanting to risk someone calling me out and him seeing me. Not until I can get my anger under control. Not until . . .

I pull my phone out and fire off a text.

Me: Go to the bathroom. Now.

I watch from afar. See her glance down to her cell when the screen lights up and then promptly turn the phone face down. She laughs at something my brother says. My fists clench at the sight of it. Another sip of wine. A slow scoot out of her chair as she makes an excuse to leave the table. Ledger standing when she does as we were taught to do.

Restaurant noises echo down the hallway. The clink of glasses. Silverware on plates. Laughter from a toast. I strain to hear the click of her heels coming down the long hallway.

But they are there. And when she passes the door of a utility closet I've stepped into, I reach out, grabbing her bicep with one hand and placing a hand over her mouth to quiet her yelp with the other before locking the door at her back.

"Callahan. What—"

Then my mouth is on hers. Desperation owns me with a violence like I've never felt before.

Fuck the rules.

Fuck the waiting.

Fuck the talking.

She's mine. Only mine. I've walked the line and done the dance and now I'm going to fucking have her.

She needs to know.

She's mine.

She freezes for the briefest of seconds, stunned that I'm here, that I'm doing this.

"Callahan. What are you—your brother—"

"Fuck my brother. This is about us. About what you said last night. About us. About wanting there to be an *us*."

"But Gia. She's here. Looking for you. I thought—"

"Gia is nothing to me. You're the only woman I want to be with, Collins. *Just you*. And I need to be inside you right fucking now."

"Yes, God, yes," she cries as I pull her close to kiss her.

The frenzy begins. Our mouths. They brand and taste and nip as if we can't get enough of each other.

Our hands. I'm unzipping my fly. She's pulling up her skirt. I'm pulling out my cock. She's yanking down her panties.

Faster.

Hurry.

Please.

Shhh.

We're a flurry of movements as I lift her ass onto the edge of the small desk in the corner and step between her spread legs. Our mouths don't stop kissing, our bodies don't stop wanting.

She wears my hand like a necklace around her throat as I hold her still against the wall at her back and push into her in one forceful stroke.

She cries out and I hope the noise of the restaurant on the other side of that door drowns it out because there is nothing that's going to fucking stop me now.

Nothing.

"Goddamn it, Collins," I groan as I'm overcome by the tight, wet heat of her pussy.

It's the heaven I've obsessed over and the hell I'll drag myself through just to feel again.

Her pulse thunders against my fingers at her throat. I lean forward and kiss her again as I start to move.

She moans words against my mouth. *God. Yes. Callahan. So good. Please. Deeper.*

Each word spurs me on as our foreheads rest against one another and our bodies become one.

I fuck her.

There are no niceties. No commands. No sweet words. Just the need and the greed and an urgency like I've never felt before.

Her fingernails dig into the wrist of my hand at her throat and her pussy squeezes tighter around my cock with each push.

"Collins," I groan as my balls pull tight and my dick grows harder.

227

"Come for me," she demands in her rasp of a voice.

And those three words fucking undo me. I lose all thought, all sense of where I am. All I can see is her. All I can feel is the crazed man she's made me. All I know is that I can't wait to fucking do it all over again.

"Mine," I murmur against her lips as I breathe her exhale as my next inhale. "Fucking mine."

CHAPTER THIRTY-THREE

Sutton

M<small>Y HEAD SPINS AS</small> I <small>WALK BACK TO THE TABLE AND TRY TO</small> fathom what the hell just happened.

The urgency. The ownership. The high of the act when getting caught was a possibility.

But more than anything, it was the look in Callahan's eyes and the emotion in his voice.

I'm not naïve to know that a lot of it was jealousy over the fact that he saw me with his brother, but there was something else there. Something more.

Wanting there to be an us.

And after thinking I screwed things up last night with my oversharing, I'll gladly take it. Gladly take *him*.

I'm on a high. From the sex. From his admission. From finally knowing there is in fact, something between us.

Now, if I can only make it through this dinner with Ledger without him knowing anything that happened over the past seven minutes.

"Ledger. Sorry. A staff member pulled me away on the way to the restroom to ask a question." I offer a polite smile as I sit down, my thighs still quivering from Callahan.

"Nothing serious, I hope."

"Nothing I couldn't handle."

"You sure? You look flushed."

My laugh is tinged with nerves. So much for trying to hide it. "Yes, I'm fine. I had to jog over to my office real quick and grab a key. Someone lost theirs and—" I shake my head. "You know what? It's not important. It's taken care of and I'm back." I offer a smile and hope it looks genuine.

He eyes me for a moment and then nods. "Okay. So where were we? We finished talking about the new offerings you want to add to the schedule, the change in marketing, which looks incredible, by the way."

"Thank you." His praise makes my smile widen. "We contracted the firm today to get going on the esthetic overhaul as well."

"I agree with your choice on them. Their design ideas were classic yet fresh. It will definitely add to the overall visual appeal of the resort when the remodel is done."

"Agreed. What else? The staff. The employees. Getting their compensation packages and contracts sorted out," I say.

"And do we have it sorted yet?"

"We've gotten a first draft of an employee contract from your team, and it's currently being negotiated. It's one of our last must-have-completed items before we leave the site."

"And it's going well? The negotiations and whatnot?"

"Nothing I can't handle," I repeat.

"Good." He nods. "That's always good to hear. Roz was right, then. We do have the right woman for the job."

If only you knew . . .

CHAPTER THIRTY-FOUR

Callahan

THE FOOTSTEPS BEHIND ME DRAW CLOSER AND THEN STOP. I don't turn around to greet him. Instead, I keep staring at the moon's reflection on the water and listening to the gentle lap of the waves on the shore.

"So let me guess. You just showing up out of the blue without warning was your way to try and catch me doing something I shouldn't be doing."

"It was a last-minute decision," Ledger says without further explanation.

"How'd you know where to find me?"

He chuckles and steps beside me so that his toes are in the sand next to where I'm sitting with a beer in hand. "I figured, what's the place most off the grid in the resort, and I went there."

I nod and take a long draw on my beer.

"Mind if I sit down?" he asks.

"Yes."

"Callahan." My name is a sigh on his lips I don't want to hear.

Not after coming down from the high of Sutton and what happened no less than two hours ago.

It wasn't enough.

Am I a selfish dick if I say that?

I've been thinking about being with her for the better part of two months and a quickie in a closet is nowhere near fucking enough of what I want from her.

What I need from her.

And that should scare the hell out of me.

But for some reason it doesn't. It only makes the desire to have her stronger. And it's not just the sex. This is where I should be freaked the fuck out.

But I'm not.

Because it's everything about her that I want more of. The sigh at her desk when she doesn't get the response she wants from whoever is on the other end of her call. The way she swings her hips past my desk to make me question the panty issue. The way she still calls me Johnnie.

And yet . . . we come from two different worlds. Two different lives.

Her and her talk of expiration dates.

Is that what I want? For us to have fun and then expire?

Isn't that all I've ever known?

Then why do I want there to be an *us*?

Is that why I'm out here trying to clear my head, to figure it all out, before facing Sutton again?

Ledger shifts his feet beside me, pulling me from my thoughts and back to him and why he's here.

"You're checking up on me," I finally say.

"Nope."

"Then you were just casually grilling Sutton over dinner to see if I've been pulling my weight and doing my part, right?"

"Callah—"

"Admit it. You're here to rub my face in whatever I've screwed up, but you're on-site and you're not finding anything wrong. So, that leaves you at a loss over what to do."

"I haven't said a word," he says.

"You didn't have to." I spit the words out, animosity eating me whole. "Oh, and by the way, should you stumble upon her, Gia conveniently happens to be here tonight. Somewhere."

His sigh is heavy. "And just like that you . . ."

"I what? I warned you she's here so you don't see her and accuse me of doing things I didn't do just like the last fucking time? Not that it's any of your goddamn business either way."

"Accuse?" He snorts.

"Yes. *Accuse.* You and Ford are so fucking hardheaded, so willing to believe the worst of me. You already had your minds made up before you even talked to me."

"Callahan. Can we just let this go? Move on?"

"No. We can't. You know why we can't? Because not once did you two ask me where I was that night."

I glance over to my brother. I used to look up to him in so many ways, and I hate that this rift between us has stripped some of that respect away. Our dad can no longer come between us, no more favoritism can eat away at our brotherly bond, but I don't know if it can be repaired.

"Just let it go, Cal."

"Fuck no." I can no longer suppress the anger burning within me. I shove up out of my seat in the sand and move to rein in that anger. "It matters because you accused me of the unforgivable. Of putting a piece of ass before our family. Of putting my needs before the good of the company. You—"

"Jesus Christ, Callahan. Cut the bullshit. You had in the past. You most likely will in the future. Why should we believe any different?"

"Ask me where I was," I shout. "*Ask me.*"

Ledger sighs and holds his hands out seeming to say, *tell me.*

"I was sitting in Dad's room all goddamn night. I was in that gray leather chair; you know the one?" Our dad used to love that chair. He'd turn it to face toward the wall of windows in his penthouse in the sky and stare at the city he loved. He'd lose hours upon hours there contemplating *world domination* he used to say. The thought brings a smile to my lips. "I turned it to face his bed so I could watch him. So I could make sure his chest would keep rising and falling with each breath. So in case it didn't, I could . . . I don't know."

Save him. Make sure he wasn't alone. I don't fucking know, but I knew I had to be there.

"Aren't you the pious son," he says.

I'm on him in a second. My hands fisted in the collar of his shirt, my face inches from his as I shout, "I'm telling the truth."

We stare at each other for a few moments, my muscles tense, my eyes begging for him to believe me.

"Callahan." It's my name. That's all it is, but hell if the way he says it and the look in his eyes doesn't tell me he might actually believe me.

"He said things at dinner that night, Ledge. Made comments. About how he wanted to go home. About seeing Mom. About how tired he was. I thought he was saying goodbye." My voice breaks, and I release my grip from his shirt and take a step back. I've spent months trying to come to terms with his death. Months. And for some reason, saying those words out loud, and having my brother really hear me, has it hit home.

He really is gone. I'll never hear his voice again. I'll never feel his solid warmth from one of his bear hugs. His laughter will never again be part of my life. *He'll never meet Sutton. Never know how much she's come to mean to me.*

God, I miss him.

I move again. Restless. I walk to the water's edge and stare out at the darkness, needing a minute to myself. Needing time to process.

Ledger walks up beside me in his quiet, stoic way, and I can see him struggling just as I am. We're Sharpes. We brush shit under the rug so when we have to sweep it out and deal with it, it's not exactly the easiest thing to do.

I scrub a hand over my face. This is not how this conversation was supposed to go. I was supposed to yell and scream and keep living in the anger that has been consuming me for months, and he was supposed to accuse and blame and keep assuming the worst of me.

But here we are. All that's missing is Ford.

"The deal," I murmur. "He begged me to allow him to sign the deal. He made me promise that we'd make this place everything Mom had wanted it to be. How we'd make it shine and worthy of the Sharpe name." I shake my head, still unable to look at him. "I was desperate to believe it wasn't the dementia talking. Desperate to hold on to that moment of clarity and believe I was doing the right thing."

"So you took the fall, let us believe you slept with Gia, so he could stay at the figurative helm."

"I couldn't let you take that from him. I've broken a lot of promises in my life, Ledge. A lot I'm not proud of, but I couldn't break that one."

"I understand." He sighs. His nod says he understands.

"The last time we talked face-to-face, you threatened to kick me out of our family business."

"I know." His words are quiet and not the anger-laced comeback I had expected.

"Is that why you're here now? To follow through on that threat?"

"There've been a lot of things said that can't be taken back," he says.

"Just like there have been a lot of things I've done, things that you and Ford were held to a different standard to than I was, that I can't take back or fix," I admit.

"It is what it is, Callahan."

"Now you sound like Dad." A bittersweet smile ghosts over my lips. I glance at him and see the tears welling in his eyes before he blinks them away and acts like they aren't there. "I resented you two, you know. We were all busy trying to live up to the Sharpe name, live up to the expectations he put in place, but you two were always better at achieving what was expected than I was and am."

"And we resented you because you were doing your own thing, and it always felt like he loved you more because of it." He looks at me. There's an honesty in his eyes that's part truth, part apology.

"I reminded him of her. That's all it was, Ledger. I reminded him of Mom, and it was his way of trying to be close to her."

He nods. "It still doesn't make it right."

"You're right. It doesn't. But at the same time, I understand it because every time I'm around you and Ford, all I see is him. In your mannerisms, in the things you say, in the disappointment you rain down on me with a single look." I take another sip of my beer. "It's hard to be around you at times. You're the golden children, and I'm the constant reminder of being the fuck-up."

"Is that why you bailed after he died?"

"I bailed for a lot of reasons. Because of the blame you put on me, because I can't stomach walking into the office and expecting to see him and knowing I never will again. Because of the guilt of not being what he needed me to be . . . because this career isn't me."

"You're good at it though."

I stare at him, take in the rare compliment and nod. "Thank you."

"You're done after this, aren't you?"

I glance his way and give a measured nod. "That was the plan."

"To where?"

"Everywhere. Somewhere. I don't really know. Somewhere I can feel alive. You know me, I get antsy if I stay in one place too long."

We fall silent as I lower myself back to the sand and hang my head, closing my eyes for a beat.

"We needed you, you know. When he died. We still do."

I nod, but don't say a word, because I don't know how his admission makes me feel. Better because maybe this rift is somewhat sewn up or worse because now that it is, I'll be walking away.

"Fuck, man. It's way easier for you to be mad at me than to have to deal with emotions and shit."

Ledger's laugh echoes around us. "Then I guess I'll add more on to the pile while we're at it."

"Jesus. Seriously?" I groan.

"He made me make him promises too, you know. Like he made you do," he says quietly and for some reason, my heart lodges in my throat at his confession.

"Ledge . . ."

"He made me promise to make you finish what you started with Ocean's Edge. *With right here.* He wanted me to use whatever means necessary to get you here, to insist you make the changes needed . . . not only to benefit the company, but so that you would know you could do it without him. That you knew you were worthy of the Sharpe name." He gives a shake of his head while tears burn in my eyes. "He said something about how he'd been teaching you all wrong. That you were the one who needed to get your hands dirty to know you'd made a difference."

I exhale audibly as I take in everything my brother has just said. Leave it to my dad to make a strong statement in death just like he had in life.

"I don't even know what to say." I lean back and look at him. "I'm sorry you were put in the position in the first place. That couldn't have been easy."

"He smiled when he asked me. He told me he'd been too much of a candy-ass over the years, but if there was one person who might be able to teach you your worth, it would be me." He stares up at the sky and pauses. "I hated him for doing it for the longest time. I hated you for putting me in the position to have to be that person . . . but coming down here, seeing you succeed, I'm not sorry at all. You've done a good job here."

"Thanks. Fuck. Can we . . . can we just leave this shit at this?" I stand up again. I move. "This is too much shrink stuff."

"I know." He chuckles. "You need to go think in peace."

"Yes. No." I hold my arms out. "Something like that."

He walks over and surprises me when he grabs onto my arm and pulls me in for a man hug. But I grab onto him with just as much force before taking a step back and smiling at him.

"Thanks . . . I guess," I tease.

"Always the smart-ass cracking a joke when things get too serious."

"You know me well, brother."

"I do." He smiles before I turn to walk away. "Hey, Callahan."

"Yeah." I stop and look over my shoulder.

"For the record, you were exactly what he needed you to be. Don't ever think anything different."

CHAPTER THIRTY-FIVE

Sutton

"AND YOU HAD NO CLUE THEY WERE DOING IT BECAUSE OF A promise they made to your dad?"

Callahan looks at me across the short distance—he's on the couch and I'm on the chair across from him—and shakes his head. "No clue."

He looks lost. That's the one constant thought I've had since he stumbled in here thirty minutes ago.

But here he sits with bloodshot eyes that I'm more than certain are from crying and a quiet posture about him that I can only chalk up to trying to process everything he's just relayed to me.

If I didn't know him any better, I'd say he looks like a defeated man, but he's not. Not after he finally hashed things out with his brother. Maybe it's that he finally faced his father's passing tonight. Maybe it's everything combined that has worn on him for so long finally being put to bed.

"What Ledger said . . . it doesn't fix everything, I know that, but at least I can walk away from everything now with a clear conscience."

I nod, not trusting myself to talk because the thought makes my chest ache. *He's leaving, Sutton. You knew that all along.* And yet there was a small part of me that was relieved tonight when he said he'd patched things up with his brother. A small part of me believed he might decide to stay if that happened.

"What's that look for?" he asks me, his head angled to the side, his eyes searching mine across the dark room.

"Nothing." I offer a soft smile that I hope reaches my eyes. "You keep telling me that you're glad this happened, that you've finally talked this all out, but I know you well enough to know something else is bugging you."

The shadows play over his features as he finds the words to voice whatever is on his mind. "I just keep asking myself what kind of man puts his family in the position that he has to be threatened to do his part? What kind of son screws up so much that his father has to put the burden on his other son to fix it?"

The heartbreak in his voice guts me. There is no right answer to his question, but I try to give one anyway. "The type of man who is trying to figure himself out. The type of man trying to find his place."

"I've done so much shit I'm not proud of." He sighs. "I'm far from perfect, Sutton."

"No one expected you to be."

Silence falls, and I stare at a man who could be broken but isn't. A man who's been through hell and is questioning his part in it. I want to wrap him in my arms and love him. I want to hold him and let him know.

"You asked me once what's in it for you. Why should we do this . . ." He looks at the ceiling as his voice fades off.

"No. Tell me, Callahan."

"There's only one answer left I can think to give but I don't think it's close to what you deserve."

"What?" I ask, my pulse picking up.

"Me." He shrugs, his eyes serious but somber. "I'm a fuck-up who is wrong more than he's right but will never admit it. I'm a spoiled rich kid who doesn't have a clue about the life you lived but wants to know. I'm a guy who needs space after he tells too much of himself and doesn't know how to face you the next day. I'm just a man, Collins. A man who doesn't deserve you but wants you anyway." He shrugs. "The answer is me."

My heart is in my throat and tears are in my eyes as he gives me the answer I never realized I wanted. The only answer I realize now I would ever accept.

I rise from my chair and move to him, and his eyes don't leave mine the entire time. Without a word and with a shy smile, I climb on the couch and straddle his thighs.

"Sutton." He breathes the word out as I run my hands up the plane of his chest to cup his face.

"Callahan," I whisper back before my lips press ever so softly to his. Almost as if I'm scared to kiss him, scared to accept the power of the emotion that's reverberating between us.

His hands trace my sides as I deepen the kiss. Whereas earlier there was an urgency to brand and claim and take, there is none of that now. There is just him and me in this darkened room with an unspoken understanding between us—we're willingly crossing the line we've flirted around.

And I'm not talking about the physical one. I'm talking emotional.

We express ourselves in movements. His hand fisting, tongues licking, and hips grinding. In soft moans and quiet pleas. In the silence no longer screaming all around us.

Along the way we lose our shirts. My bra. His pants are shoved down and my skirt is pulled up and over my head.

There is quiet desperation to our movements now. To knowing what is going to happen and anticipating that bliss.

"Christ, you're beautiful," Callahan says as he kisses a line down my neck and takes one of my nipples in his mouth. "To touch you. To feel you. To have you . . ."

His last word falls off on a strangled groan when I sink down onto him, inch by inch, until he's fully seated within me.

"Look at me," he whispers. My eyes flutter up to meet his. To take in the look on his face. The pained pleasure. The desperate longing. The want that's now turned into need.

I begin to move. To rock my hips back and forth over his. To keep my eyes locked on his even when I want to close them and give in to the pleasure surging through me.

"Do you know how much I missed this?" he says, leaning forward and slanting his lips over mine once again. "Missed you?"

I want to tell him I've been here all along, but I haven't. He's right. This is different. *Right now is different.* We are different and hell if it isn't the headiest thing I've ever experienced.

We move in a slow, luxurious sync. Our hips grinding, our tongues tangling, and our bodies slowly whirling in the eddy of pleasure together.

He lets me control the pace. A deepening of the kiss as I rise and then slowly lower myself back down onto his cock. I grind my hips, letting him feel how wet he's made me. Letting him know how much he turns me on.

He palms both cheeks of my ass and then guides me back up again. I tighten my muscles almost as if my body is desperate for us not to part. His groan at the sensation is sensual foreplay. It's a sexy rumble that turns into a growled sigh when I seat myself back down on him once again.

We move like this for some time. There are no words. No whispered promises. Just him needing and me wanting.

I feel like I can't get enough of his touch. Of his taste. Of his soft groans that wash over me. Of the ecstasy when he slides in and out of me.

I just want him. More of him. All of him. Endless amounts of him.

There is no hurry as our bodies climb and then crash over the edge. His guttural groan as I pulse around him and he empties himself in me.

And when we follow each other to his bed afterwards, we know that without uttering a single word, things have irrevocably changed between us.

Making love a second time only cements that. The way he worships my body and caters to my pleasure leaves me at a further loss for words.

And when I fall asleep, curled up against him in the early hours of the morning, there is only one constant stream of thought.

Regret.

That I waited this long to do this with him.

That our time is limited.

That . . . I've fallen for him when I know there's no future.

That we have an expiration date.

CHAPTER THIRTY-SIX

Sutton

"STAY IN BED," CALLAHAN MURMURS AGAINST THE TOP OF MY head when I startle awake.

"It's early. Where are—"

"I'm going to drive my brother to the airport." A soft kiss on my lips. "When I come back, I want to find you in exactly the same place as you are right now."

"Callahan." I sit up and stare at his silhouette in the open doorway. He turns to look at me with a soft smile. His hair is wet and wavy from the shower.

He nods ever so slightly, almost as if to tell me, yes, he is coming back.

And even though I know he is, I stay staring at the empty doorway long after I hear the front door shut.

I put my fingers to my lips as if I can still feel his kiss. But I don't need to touch them to feel it.

I don't think I'll ever forget it. *Or him.*

With a sigh, I flop back on the bed and wrap sheets that smell like him around me.

You get one hour to feel sorry for yourself, Sutton. One hour to be angry at yourself for waiting so long to let this happen. One hour to cry about what's never going to be.

You knew this going in to whatever this is.

You knew he wasn't staying.

You knew he wasn't a keeper.

Then why is the little voice in my head saying, "But you knew all this before you really knew him at all . . ."

CHAPTER THIRTY-SEVEN

Callahan

I SIT IN THE CAR AND WATCH LEDGER'S PLANE TAKE OFF FROM THE airport until it's a speck of silver in the pinks and oranges of the morning sunrise.

With my hand on the steering wheel and my head leaned back against the seat, I try to unpack the past twenty-four hours.

But how is that even possible?

How do you process your world being rocked? How do you lay down the anger you've worn like armor for the past year without feeling like you're missing something? And how do you fathom going home to slide into bed with a woman when all you've ever done is slip out of one quietly to avoid complication?

"Fuck," I mutter to myself as I chew the inside of my cheek. Is this what normalcy feels like? A family that's working on things, a woman you can't wait to be with, and a job that takes up the space between?

The sun rises. Slowly. Steadily. It rises over the horizon with a quiet beauty like always.

Which horizon will I be watching it from in the coming weeks? What beach, what country, what mountaintop will I be admiring it from?

The thought used to bring me peace in the early days of this venture. It used to be my fallback to get me through.

Then why does it sound less appealing now?

Why does it seem less ...everything?

CHAPTER THIRTY-EIGHT

Sutton

"I T'S ALL THE MIND-BLOWING SEX YOU'RE HAVING."
I glance up and grin at Callahan standing at the foot of the couch where I'm currently curled up in a blanket despite the gorgeous weather outside. "Oh, really?"

"Yep." He takes a seat on its edge and pats my thigh. "You've exerted so much energy over the past few days that your body has caught a case of sex-itis."

I snort despite my misery.

"I have sore muscles."

"From all the new positions we've tried."

"And a fever," I add.

"I've always thought you were hot." He shrugs unapologetically.

"And a sore throat."

"Next time don't take me so deep. I know I'm big." He fights his grin. "I apologize if it's stretched you too wide and your tonsils hate me."

I roll my eyes. "I assure you that's not it."

"Any other symptoms I can diagnose?"

"Just general *bleh*. How are you going to diagnose that, smarty-pants?"

He brushes my hair off my forehead. "The general *bleh* is a manufactured symptom whereas the patient complains about malaise—"

"Malaise?" I lift my eyebrows. "I'm impressed."

"You should be. But please, let me finish my diagnosis." He leans over and presses a kiss to my forehead. "The complaints about malaise are simply a ruse because they are too embarrassed to admit that their man has more stamina than they do."

"My man?" I laugh out.

"Yes. That would be me."

"And the cure?"

"Dick."

I burst out laughing. "So let me get this straight. The sickness is from too much dick and the cure is more dick?"

"Correct. That's what all my schooling tells me." He angles his head and studies me. "Seriously though, get some rest."

"I feel like I should be there. Solomon—"

"Can be tricky, yes." He nods. "But I assure you I'm not worried."

"You sure? I mean—"

"Sutton. I'm a big boy. I've got it handled."

"Okay. Yes. Tucking away my control freak tendencies as we speak."

He tucks the blanket around my feet more. "Get some rest. I'll report back with good news."

I watch him grab his laptop and files full of papers and wonder how in the hell we went from meeting in a bar to this.

Like how is that possible?

I blow out a breath and snuggle deeper in the blanket, my head foggy (Callahan would say it's because it's filled with thoughts of dick), and my mind running over the whirlwind of the past few days since A.L.—After Ledger.

Because everything has changed since then. Yes, we are still keeping things secretive and on the down-low, but there is no more purposeful avoidance when the other is at the villa. There are sexy texts sent back and forth while I'm sitting at my desk and he's in his office, and then later, strategically planned departures from said office. There are late night "working" dinners delivered from The Cove to the villa so we can laugh and talk and tease out of sight of everyone else.

And there is a lack of sleep. So much sleep lost . . . but this girl definitely isn't complaining.

Not at all.

But the clock is counting down, the days here are numbered, and as much as I'm trying not to think about it, I'm still thinking about it.

Stop it, Sutt.

No pity.

All party.

CHAPTER THIRTY-NINE

Callahan

THERE'S A THRILL IN THE ART OF NEGOTIATION. IN SITTING FACE to face with a smug bastard like Solomon and challenging him over and over to validate the demands he was championing for.

Keone was definitely right, though. Trouble was brewing amongst the Ocean's Edge staff. Wage complaints, benefit grumbles, and just issues in general about shifts and overtime.

With Brady explaining the lay of the land regarding what other resorts are offering and Keone telling us what's being said in private amongst the staff, Sutton and I were able to bring what we thought was a fair and comprehensive employment package to the table. Higher wages, more perks for the staff, guaranteed one weekend day off unless otherwise specified, matching 401(k) up to six percent, and on and on.

Of course, *we* thought it was fair. Solomon, on the other hand, did his job handily over the past three hours, trying to advocate for more, more, more for the staff.

Some things I budged on.

Others, not an inch.

I still might not care for Solomon, but I think we both left the table with a solid agreement that is good for both the employees and Sharpe International.

"Boss Man." Keone chuckles. "What are you doing here midday? Your day that bad you need a drink already?"

"No drink. I can't stay," I say, hitting my fist on the bar. "But I wanted to thank you for the heads-up on the staff rumblings."

"Oh yeah? Me?" Keone wipes his hands on a towel, a crooked smile on his lips. "I helped?"

"You did. And I appreciate it. I wanted to say thank you. New contracts and benefits will be offered by the week's end."

"No shit?"

"No shit."

"You going to see your lady now?"

I falter at his words. My reaction a dead giveaway that I am. But how does he know?

"What do you mean?" I feign innocence.

"You're a different man these last couple days. You do this job long enough you know the signs of a man who's happy." He puts his hands on his hips and smiles. "It's not the redhead, is it? Jessica Rabbit? The one who came here and you play hard to get with?"

I laugh at his description of Gia Diamante and shake my head. "No. It's not Jessica Rabbit. But that's a good one."

"Man, whoever she is, she must be good if you passing up that."

I just grin and wink. "Later, Ke. Thanks again."

Man, she must be good if you passing up that.

He has no idea.

And the thought pervades as I walk into the villa and find Sutton sitting there with expectant eyes looking my way. "Well?" She pats the cushion on the couch beside her.

"It's done."

She squeals in laughter. "It's done as in the agreement is done, or it's done as in the agreement is signed?"

Sutton looks at me with shock on her face and fuck if my ego doesn't soar. "As in signed, signed."

"No way."

"Truth." I hold my hands up.

"I was waiting to hear sirens because you'd reached across the table and strangled him for being an ass but then felt guilty for doing so, so you called 911."

I take a seat beside her. "I may have done that mentally once or twice." My smile widens. "But it's done, Collins. We agreed on all terms. I gave a little. He gave a lot. The deal is done. In fact, the agreements are being written up for all members of staff, and Brady will have them delivered by the end of the week."

She stares at me with her jaw lax and eyes wide and it fills me with such a sense of purpose that I never knew I needed or wanted.

"I'm so proud of you. That's incredible. We should celebrate . . ." She laughs. "When I feel better of course."

"Nope. We're not waiting. Who says we can't celebrate when you're sick?" I link my fingers with hers. "There's a lot to be said for sitting on the couch, putting your feet up on the table, and eating candy by the handfuls straight from oversized bags."

"You're serious, aren't you?"

"Dead serious." I hook a thumb over my shoulder. "What did you think was in the bags?" I rise from the couch. "Pick a movie and I'll go get changed real quick."

"Hey?" Sutton says and tugs on my hand before I can walk away.

"What?"

She has more color in her cheeks than when I left her. Her eyes a little less glassy. She smiles softly. "You know you're good at this, right? Have you ever considered that you love the job but not the part you've been given to do?"

"Sutton." Her name is a sigh.

"Hear me out and I won't mention it again." She lifts her eyebrows as if pleading for me to agree.

"Fine. What?"

"You've always dealt with everything on the macro level of this business, but I've sat here, day in and day out, and watched you work on the micro level and do an absolutely phenomenal job." She squeezes my fingers. "Maybe that's your niche. The on-site details of making a deal work instead of the broad overview of one. The devil is in the details, Callahan, and you seem to know how to deal with them."

I nod and head toward the bedroom.

"It's a shame you're going to walk away from something you're so skilled at," she says.

I hear her. But I don't respond. Can't. Because I'm not one hundred percent sure how her words make me feel.

And it's not until later, when her head is resting on my chest where she fell asleep during the movie, that I allow myself to think about her words again.

That I allow myself to wonder if she might be right.

But it doesn't matter if she's right or wrong because I have plans a little over a week from now. I'm going to close my eyes and put a finger on a map of the world and that's where I'll end up.

Just like I've wanted to for some time.

At least this time I can do it without any guilt for not fulfilling my promise to my brothers.

But what about Sutton?

I close my eyes and listen to her soft breathing and rationalize my thoughts away.

"You know that, don't you? What a good man you are? That's why I've fallen for you."

There's no promise to break with her because I never made one in the first place.

Keep telling yourself that, Sharpe.

Keep telling yourself that and you might actually believe you're not falling for her too.

CHAPTER FORTY

Sutton

"WHERE ARE YOU TAKING ME?" I LAUGH AS HE PARKS THE topless Jeep in an empty parking lot on the opposite side of the island from Ocean's Edge.

"Don't worry about it." He reaches out a hand to me. "Just come with me."

We trek down a trail where native plants tangle around our legs, and we have to push them away so they don't hit our faces. Our laughter is the only sound as I follow him until I utter a soft "Oh," when we reach the clearing.

We're on a small patch of beach where a hammock hangs between what looks like two strategically placed palm trees. And the hammock is set up to overlook a small sand bluff above the sea. To the left is a pile of rocks that I have to give a double take because of their precarious stacking that gives the illusion of a man's profile. But best of all, is the view I can already tell it will have of the sunset.

"Callahan." I take a few steps forward and admire the view. "This is breathtaking."

"It is, isn't it?" He steps up beside me. "Our wine vendor told me about it at one of my dinner meetings. It's a friend of a friend of his who owns the land or something like that."

"Just when I thought this place couldn't get any more incredible, you give me this."

A shy smile ghosts over his lips and our gazes hold. "I can't exactly take you out on a date because people might see us—and on this island, everybody knows somebody—but I can give you this." He holds up the bag he's carrying in his hand. "Some wine. Some cheese and crackers. A sunset. And some company to enjoy it with."

"I'd like that." The words are hard to get out, and I'm so grateful my voice doesn't relay the emotion swelling inside of me.

Our days are numbered. He knows that, I know that, but we've yet to address the huge elephant in the room.

We make small talk as we sip wine and eat. We give theories about how the rocks were stacked just so and discuss how relieved Brady is going to be to have us out of his hair when we're gone. We talk about Keone and his astute instincts. We discuss my top-ten list and what are my favorites for reasons other than business.

Small talk.

Insignificant.

Filling space.

And when the sky turns deep pinks, purples, and oranges as the sun begins to dip, we both lean back in the hammock next to each other, his arm behind my head and wrapped around my shoulders. We fall into a comfortable silence.

The breeze whirls around us as Mother Nature puts on a show.

"I'm sorry our last days have been me being sick and you taking care of me," I finally say. "Thank you."

He presses a kiss on the crown of my head. "To be honest, I've enjoyed hanging at the villa with you. We've spent so much of our time here avoiding being at the same place at the same time, that it was just nice being with you without having to watch every look I give you or word I say to you. No outside noise. Just you. Just me."

"It has," I murmur, enjoying the steady beat of his heart beneath my ear where it rests on his chest. The sun keeps falling, and I keep waiting to find the courage to bring that elephant front and center.

There are five days left, and we've yet to say a freaking word about what happens after that.

And while I know that expiration date looms, I still need to hear it from him. I still need to hear the tone of his voice and feel like I matter. Like this matters. Because every part of me feels that I do, that it does, but it feels like Callahan is purposely ignoring it so he doesn't have to face it.

Bite the bullet, Sutton.

"So have you decided where you're off to after this?" I ask. Definitely not the question I need to voice, but it's a start.

"Not yet." He runs a finger up and down my arm. He hesitates as if he has more to say, but nothing comes.

"I'm sure wherever you'll go, you'll find what you need there." I try to keep the sadness from my voice, try to prevent the tears that are welling from spilling over . . . try to keep it together. "Wine," I say and awkwardly get out of the hammock. "I need more wine."

I occupy my fidgeting hands by pouring more wine into my glass but not even taking a sip of it. He shifts behind me. I hear his footsteps in the sand, but I keep my eyes focused on the sunset in front of us.

Ask me to go.

Tell me you'll stay.

Say something.

"This doesn't have to be it, Collins," he says, as my heart constricts in my chest. "I'll be in and out of Manhattan. The States. We can make this work. We can—"

I turn and put a finger on his lips to stop him. His eyes search mine. They are laden with an earnestness, a hope, I never expected to see, so this only makes it harder for me to do what I need to do.

He's saying the words I wanted to hear, but deep down, I know they're just words. Deep down I know I deserve more, better . . . *everything.*

So much has changed in such a short time for me that I'm not afraid to raise the bar for myself. I spent years with Clint, afraid to want more, to aspire for more because I feared his reaction to it.

But I look at the man before me. The handsome, powerful man standing here who thinks he's callous and selfish and without purpose, but who I know to be the exact opposite. He's empowering and encouraging and has helped instill a confidence in me that I've never had before. A self-assurance that I'm not ashamed of.

He's shown me it's okay to want more. That there is nothing wrong with that.

And even more importantly, I know I can voice that confidence right now without fear of being belittled for it.

Deep down, I know he'll understand why I'm about to say the things I need to say.

Even if my heart is breaking while I do so.

"It's okay, Callahan. You don't have to make promises you don't intend to keep," I say. *Breathe, Sutton.* "We both walked into whatever this is knowing that there was an expiration date to us—"

"Fucking Brady," he mutters and laughs.

"He's right though, and that's okay." I smile and stroke the side of his cheek. I want to choke on every single word I'm saying. Words I know he needs to hear, that I need to say, but that will only serve to devastate my heart. "You've waited your whole life to have freedom and wings to fly." I lean up on my toes and brush a tender kiss to his lips. "Go fly, Callahan."

He shakes his head, confusion suddenly in his eyes. "You could come with me then. We could travel and—"

"I can't," I whisper, my voice more than breaking this time as I steel myself from the want to say yes and the need to say no. "I put my aspirations on hold and my happiness in someone's hands before. I can't do that to myself again. I'm on the cusp of achieving so much that I've worked for that I have to look out for me." The first tear slips over and his expression falls at the sight of it.

"Sutton." He cups my face, and I press my lips into his palm, closing my eyes for a beat.

"The problem is that I know I'd wait for you. Because *you*, Callahan Sharpe, are worth waiting for. I'd wait and take the little scraps you throw my way when you come into town, but I deserve more than that. I deserve the things you aren't ready to give yet and so . . . I'm sorry."

"Don't be." He offers me a crooked smile, a brave face, and I feel better knowing he's hurting too.

He leans in and presses the most bittersweet of kisses to my lips before wrapping his arms around me and pulling me in.

We stand like this for some time.

Breathing each other in.

Holding each other tight.

Reveling in the moment while regretting the ones that we know we'll have to deal with in the coming days. I've known him such a short time, but I know he'll be taking my heart with him when he leaves. In a bittersweet twist, knowing him has helped me grow enough to be certain that saying no is the best thing for me. Long-term. And hopefully for him too.

He does deserve to fly.

And I deserve to soar too.

CHAPTER FORTY-ONE

Callahan

I WATCH HER SLEEPING. THE RISE OF HER CHEST. THE SOFT EXHALE out. And my chest hurts in a way I've never felt it hurt before.

I close my eyes and prepare myself for the lie I'm about to tell.

For being the chickenshit I'm about to be.

For walking away this way instead of a long, drawn-out goodbye, because it hurts too fucking much to be with her and know I won't be in a few days' time.

I glance over to where my bags are packed, waiting at the front door, before I sit on the bed beside her and brush the hair off her forehead.

"Sutton." My voice is broken already on her name. "Sutt."

Her lashes flutter open in the early morning light. Alarm flashes through her eyes. "What—is—"

"Shh." I lean forward and kiss her lips. "Everything is okay." I lean my forehead against hers and just breathe. "I have to go." Her body stills. "I've been called back to meetings. I . . ."

"No." It's a soft sigh of disbelief that has her hands reaching up to touch my face.

"I know." I choke the words out. "I'm sorry." And those two words are for so much more than for how I'm leaving.

They're for not being man enough to stay.

For not being the man she deserves.

For not realizing any of this sooner.

"Callahan," she murmurs as she brings her lips to mine. "Please." She kisses me again. "Not yet."

I lean back and see the tear escape the corner of her eye and fall to the pillow beneath her head. It stomps on my heart that already feels like it's breaking. "I know." I press my lips to hers again. "I know," I say between kisses. "I know." I repeat it as we both strip our clothes off with a quiet urgency. "I know," I whisper, as I push my way into her and begin the process of saying goodbye.

It's her eyes on mine as we move together.

It's her fingers linked with mine as I try to show her what she means to me.

It's her name on my lips as I try to memorize the look on her face.

We say goodbye in the early morning light with the palm trees rustling in the breeze outside and with what feels like a hurricane of emotion raging inside me.

We say goodbye with quiet kisses and gentle sighs.

We say goodbye after I'm dressed again, her body pressed against mine as I hold her there and kiss the top of her head.

We speak in looks, in tender kisses, in a glance over my shoulder to where she stands in the hallway before I walk out the door and out of her life.

The image of her sticks with me as the driver takes me to the tarmac where the Sharpe International private jet awaits me.

It's all I see as the jet takes off, Ocean's Edge Resort a shrinking speck beneath me.

I'm such an asshole for doing it this way.

For being this way.

For proving her right.

She does deserve better than me.

"Maybe one day you'll fall in love and bring her to this place too, Callahan. Your mother would love that."

"I did, Dad," I murmur below the hum of the jet's engines before leaning my head back in my seat and closing my eyes.

But I didn't know how to keep her.

CHAPTER FORTY-TWO

Sutton

IN THE DISTANCE I HEAR THE ROAR OF A JET OVERHEAD. IT'S TOO early for commercial flights so I know it's him. Callahan Sharpe. *My Johnnie Walker.*

I love you.

Those three words repeat in my head just as they were on the tip of my tongue when he looked over his shoulder and met my eyes one last time.

I know he wasn't called back early for meetings.

I know because if that were the case, Ledger would have told me that when I talked to him last night on the phone. When I set up a meeting with him in the office in Manhattan for the coming week.

Callahan left to make it easier on him . . . on me . . . on *what?* I have no idea.

While I'm hurting, I'm almost grateful to him for doing it this way. Long goodbyes are brutal and he just saved us that.

But he also proved to me that I'm right in my decision.

That I need to put myself first, because with Callahan Sharpe, I'd be at his whim. I'd be the one left behind when things got too real, and he didn't know how to deal with them.

I pick up my phone to text Lizzy, to tell her what just happened, but my fingers don't move.

Maybe I don't want to believe it yet. Maybe I need to just sit in the silence for a bit more and have the moment to myself to realize this really is over. That he really is gone.

That I really did love him.

"Goodbye, Callahan," I whisper into the silence. "Thank you for helping me find me again. Thank you for loving me regardless."

CHAPTER FORTY-THREE

Sutton

"I GET TO SEE YOU IN HOURS," LIZZY YELLS INTO THE PHONE, making me laugh.

And the laugh is most definitely needed because I've just said goodbye to everyone at Ocean's Edge. It was much harder than expected.

And maybe it was even harder because my heart was already wounded to begin with.

"I know. I've missed you." My smile is bittersweet as the driver takes me to the airport.

"We have so much to catch up on."

"So much." I try to infuse happiness in my voice, but fuck, it's hard to do.

"Are you sure you don't need to stay here at my place?"

"No. The Sharpes have offered me their suite for a week or two until I can find a place of my own." I shake my head, trying to understand how this all unfolded. The call from Ledger temporarily offering the suite to me since he knows I've been out of town for months and probably need time to find a new place to live.

And me taking it. While I can't wait to spend time with Lizzy, I also need to unwind and sort through everything on my own.

Time alone will allow me to do that.

"Oh," she says. "They are *so* trying to schmooze you to leave Roz and come work for them doing this full-time."

"They are not."

"Bullshit." She snorts. "How do you feel about the possibility?" Her voice softens. Seeing as she was the shoulder I cried on over the past few days, she knows everything.

"I don't know. Honestly. I just don't know." I glance around one last time at the beaches as we drive past. "It's not like he's going to be there. Hell, by now he's probably in Tonga or somewhere like that. It's just . . ."

"Give yourself time to figure it out."

"I will. I promise, I will."

I've had three days of silence since Callahan left. I'm not sure why I hoped for him to at least reach out with a call or a text, but I should know better.

I've never minded quiet before, but the silence left by his absence has been almost unbearable. And while the two of us started off our time at Ocean's Edge in weird territory, he was always here. Always talking. Always a presence I couldn't ignore.

Having an all-access pass to him once we were behind the villa's doors the past few weeks has made this even harder. Knowing what I'm missing. His laughter. His glance across the room. His soft smile. His tender and demanding touch.

His friendship, more than anything.

I emit a quiet sigh to try and control the tears welling in my eyes. The same tears I've fought every moment since he departed.

I've missed him more than I thought possible.

"We're here," my driver says.

And when I look up, the car is pulling through the gates of the airport and up to a jet parked on the far end that says Sharpe International on it.

Lizzy's right.

They definitely are trying.

The question is, what am I going to do about it?

CHAPTER FORTY-FOUR

Sutton

I GO THROUGH THE MOTIONS AT WORK UPON MY RETURN. The debriefing with Roz. The company-wide meeting she calls where she praises me and the whole staff claps in celebration. The one-on-one with her afterwards where she pats my back and offers me a promotion.

It's everything I strove for and yet when I stand in Sharpe International's suite after a long day, all I feel is empty inside.

Yes, there will be more jobs to immerse myself in. Yes, there will be more locations to fall in love with. But I know that Ocean's Edge will always hold a special place in my heart.

I have what I wanted, I achieved the goal I set for myself, but sitting in this luxurious hotel room, all I can think about is him. About that first night. About everything that happened since and wonder *what if*.

What if I dare to want more?

What if I don't settle?

What if I had said yes to Callahan?

But none of it does me any good.

And late at night when I snuggle into the expensive sheets in this luxurious bed, I pretend he's here with me.

And I smile through the tears.

CHAPTER FORTY-FIVE

Sutton

I'T'S LIKE DÉJÀ VU SITTING HERE IN THIS IMPOSING CONFERENCE room.

Nerves still rattle and my pulse still pounds, but it's for completely different reasons this time.

"We're offering you a full-time position at Sharpe International," Ledger says, his hands clasped in front of him.

Ford nods and smiles. "We're more than impressed with the role you played in turning Ocean's Edge around. It's been, what? Eleven weeks since you began working there and we're already seeing an uptick in reservations and secondary spending for our periphery items. The staff surveys are positive and with the interior renovation set to begin in a few weeks' time, we think that once that is complete, we'll achieve an even larger return on our investment than we expected."

"That's great news." I smile. "But it wasn't all me, I assure you. You have great staff there, and Callahan was an excellent partner to work with."

I'm not blind to the glance that Ledger gives Ford. Is it because they miss him being here with the company? Is it because they are glad he's gone? Is it because they think I'm covering for him? I wring my hands where they sit in my lap beneath the table.

"We've told him as much the last time we spoke with him."

Where is he?

What is he doing now?

I take a deep breath, push my emotions aside, and quiet the questions

I want to shout at them but can't. "He'll probably be pleased to hear that. *Or pissed,*" I say. "It can go either way with him."

They both laugh while I dance an awkward tightrope and try to figure out how to act.

"So, the job offer," Ledger redirects. "We know Roz has given you a promotion as she should have after the excellent work you did for us, but we're greedy. We want you for ourselves." He smiles. "Of course, compensation and the like would all be negotiable, but I assure you it would be a fair share higher than Roz's."

"I'm sure somewhere in the contract you signed with her, there'd be a non-compete or whatever technical term there is for it," I say, caught completely off guard and fumbling to buy some time so my brain can process the question he just asked.

"There is," Ford says with a nod. "But rest assured, Roz and the firm would be taken care of with other projects of ours to make up for the loss of you."

"Bribery." I chuckle nervously.

"Compensation," Ford says with a resolute nod that is equal parts arrogance and privilege and so much like Callahan's that my chest constricts at the sight of it. "We're not in the habit of screwing over the people who work with us. I assure you."

"So . . ." Ledger asks.

I suck in a breath and meet both Ledger's and then Ford's expectant gazes. I can't do it. There's no way I can work with these two men, day in and day out, and be reminded of the love I can't have.

It also means I would hold out hope for Callahan. To see him on the off times we happen to be in this office at the same time. To talk to him somehow, someway. That he would decide to stay put for good and be with me.

And I can't do that when I told myself I wouldn't settle again.

"Gentlemen. Thank you for the offer. I'm flattered and astounded by it." I glance down at the table before looking back up to the brothers. "But I have to decline it."

"What?" Ledger laughs. Just like his brother, it seems the word *no* isn't something he hears very often.

I think of my talks with Roz over the past few weeks. Of explaining my aspirations to her to step out on my own someday. Her nervous laughter after my confession and then her wide eyes when she realized I was serious.

"Why are you telling me this? Most people would fear I'd fire them, knowing their ultimate goal is to use me to build their reputation and then leave me to be a competitor." She stares at me behind the black frames of her glasses.

"I'm telling you because you are a strong female business owner. One who took the same leap ten years ago, and I figured if anyone would understand my drive to succeed, you would."

Roz stares at me with a guarded expression that I can't quite read. "You want to do this?"

I nod.

"It's a lot of long thankless hours. Hours spent behind a desk instead of on location being hands-on, like you just were."

I think of Callahan, it's hard not to, thinking about how he loathed the behind the desk part but was so good at being on location.

Do I want the same thing? Can I thrive in an office now that I've had a taste of what else I'm capable of?

"It's something I want to work toward. Learning the ins and outs of every facet over the coming year—if you'll allow me the chance, of course—so that I take the leap if that's what I decide I still want."

"You think you'll be ready to take the jump after a year?"

"No one's ever ready, but sometimes you have to jump and then learn how to fly," I say.

"Sutton Pierce." Roz's smile widens. "I don't know what happened to you down in the Virgin Islands—the confidence, the directness, the drive—but I'm loving it. I'll gladly mentor you."

Callahan did. He's what happened to me.

But I can't say that to anyone other than Lizzy.

"My goal has always been to have my own firm. To work for myself. Over the past few weeks, and from the experience you've afforded me with Ocean's Edge, I know now more than ever that that's what I want to accomplish."

Another glance is exchanged between the two. "Playing hardball right out of the gate," Ford says with a laugh. "Then let us be your first and only client. Be our exclusive consultant. Let us help you build a strong portfolio."

"I . . ." I laugh, overwhelmed. *Did he really just say that?* That he'd take care of Roz and hire me as an independent contractor, let me work for Sharpe International and only Sharpe International, while building my portfolio and making connections for the future? That's like a dream scenario.

What's the catch?

There has to be a catch.

And then I look from Ford to Ledger and know exactly what the catch is—*them.* I'd have a daily reminder of the man I love. The man who walked away. It'd be like having him so close I could touch him, but knowing I can't have him.

"You're not responding," Ledger says.

"Why would you do that for me?" I finally ask.

"Because good people are hard to find, Sutton. And you've more than proven that you are just that, good at what you do . . . so while it might benefit you, we are the ones who get the most out of it."

"I'm flattered. And thank you. I'm a little overwhelmed. I mean, Roz . . . What would—"

"Like we said, we'd handle her," Ledger says.

"Still, I . . ."

"We know we've given you a lot to think about," Ford says with a gentle smile. "Would you like a few moments to consider our proposal?"

"Yes. Please." My hands tremble so I clasp them to try and hide it from them. "I'd appreciate that."

They gather their laptops and papers and smile as they exit the conference room, leaving me sitting there dumbfounded.

I need to move, to process . . . to think. Rising from my chair, I move toward the wall of windows and stare out at the city below but don't really see anything. I'm too busy realizing everything I wanted career wise is just within reach but so terrifyingly close to what I can't have.

"Did we give you enough time?" Ledger asks as he walks into the conference room after what feels like only seconds. "Or do you need more?"

I lower my eyes to look at my hands and sigh. "I'm sorry. I appreciate the offer and your faith in me, but at this time, I don't think it would be the best decision—"

"*I wouldn't do that if I were you.*"

My whole body stills as I hear those words. Words that were spoken to me the first time Callahan and I ever met. I'm afraid to hope he's here, afraid to look up and see if he is.

And if I do and he is, there's no way in hell I'm going to be able to keep the emotion off my face. There's absolutely no way I'll be able to keep what we *had* a secret from his brothers.

"Look at me, *Collins.*"

My chest tightens at that silly name spoken by an incredible man.

I swallow over the hopeful trepidation lodged in my throat and dare to look up. Tears well in my eyes, but there he is. "Callahan." His name is a reflex and an oath I'm bound to keep.

Ledger looks from his brother, to me, and then pats Callahan on the back as he walks out of the conference room, shutting the door behind him.

"They know," he says when I'm certain panic blankets my face.

"They know?"

He nods and takes a step toward me. "I told them everything. Minus the details they don't need to know, of course." He winks, and I try to understand why he has a smile on his face when I'm struggling to breathe. To hope. To not want.

"But . . . *why?*"

"Why what?" he asks.

"Why did you tell them?" I whisper.

"Because I had to. Because I figured if I was staying here then I needed to come clean with them. And—"

"What do you mean if you were staying here?" The first tear slips over, and I wipe it off my cheek.

"All I've ever wanted is to get out of this place, to be free, and then when I had the opportunity to do so, I just couldn't do it."

My heart races. My hands tremble. But I ask the question anyway. "Why not?"

He closes the distance between us and lowers his head to my level as he cradles my face in his hands. His eyes, that liquid amber, gaze into mine and he smiles warmly. "Because I had other, more important things on my mind."

"Like?"

"Like you are looking at the new Vice President of On-site Transition for Sharpe International Network." His smile beams. "Someone wise once pointed out that I'm good at the micro aspect of this job. I took her words to heart and propositioned my brothers."

"Propositioned?"

"I'll get to be out of the office and on-site. I'll get to travel. I'll get to be part of my legacy, but make my own niche while doing so."

"That's incredible. But what about your dreams to travel? What about—"

"Those are things I still want, Collins, but I want *you* more."

"What?" I ask with confusion, almost as if I didn't hear him. "What are you saying?"

"I'm saying Brady's wrong."

"Brady?" I laugh.

"I don't like expiration dates. I don't want one with you."

"Callahan. Don't—"

His lips are on mine in the softest, most tender kiss that feels like a caress against every single one of my nerve endings. "Shh. The answer to the question, Collins—to what's in it for you—is *us*." A kiss on my cheek where another tear has slipped over.

"*Us?*" I ask like an idiot. My head is spinning and my heart is swelling.

"Us." He nods. "I have a different proposition for you."

Oh God. Oh no. Not yet. And he must see the panic in my face because he throws his head back and starts laughing.

"I'm not asking you to marry me, Collins. Let's not go that crazy just yet."

I breathe out a huge sigh, and then start laughing until I look up and see his arms crossed over his chest and an eyebrow raised. "Would it be so bad?" he asks.

I lean forward and kiss his mouth, my lips spreading into a smile against his. "No. No, it wouldn't but don't give a girl multiple heart attacks in one day." I laugh again and rest my forehead against his. "What is this proposition you speak of?"

"Ledger's offer—*our offer*—still stands. Start your company, be your own boss, but let us be your client. Let us help you build your portfolio."

"And . . ."

"And as the new VP, I have some serious demands."

"Oh really?" My cheeks hurt from smiling so hard. From nerves to tears to grinning. Talk about an unexpected emotional roller coaster. This was definitely not how I expected this meeting to go. "What are they?"

"That you must be on-site with me. That we work as partners. *As equals*. No more hiding. No more granny panties."

I hiccup over a part sob, part laugh as amusement wells in his eyes. *And love.*

I thought I'd seen it before but was afraid to hope it was true.

Now I see it, and it's the most heart-stopping thing I've ever seen.

"You're serious," I whisper.

"Dead serious. We make a good team, Collins. That and I don't plan on letting you out of my sight anytime soon, so two birds, one stone."

"You think you have it all figured out, don't you?"

"I know I do."

"Whatever happened to good, old-fashioned negotiations?" I quirk an eyebrow.

His laugh is low and deep. "There is no negotiating when it comes to us. Ever."

"Ever?"

He presses a kiss to my lips. "Ever."

EPILOGUE

Sutton

One Year Later

THE SOUND OF LAUGHTER ECHOING FROM THE OUTSIDE PATIO makes me smile. It's hard for me to decipher whose laugh is whose because when the three of them are together like this, they sound the same.

Another laugh sounds off and my heart swells in my chest.

Who knew these weekends away at their father's estate in Sag Harbor would further heal the wounds and strengthen the bonds they have been mending over the past twelve months?

Their agreement to meet here once a month, away from the office, with the promise of no talk about work while they slowly go through their father's things he left behind, hasn't wavered.

Every month they come.

Every month they go through pieces of their past and learn more of their father's history.

Every month they grow closer.

I peek out the open French doors to watch them. Callahan is sitting forward, his elbows on his knees, a beer in one hand, his smile wide. Ledger sits across from him in a similar position, while Ford is pushing photographs out of a box across the table toward them.

Photos their father had kept over the years. Moments captured that allow them to reminisce or learn something new altogether.

It's the first time Callahan has asked me to come along on his monthly helicopter flight out here. I told him I didn't want to come. That him being here with his brothers was more important than anything.

He insisted.

"We've gone through all the legal, hard-to-deal-with stuff. We've hashed out our differences on that. This weekend we're going through pictures."

"I still don't feel right. Like it's an invasion of privacy," I say.

"I want you there, Collins." He kisses me and pulls me against him. "I need you there."

And even though I feared Ledger and Ford might resent me being here, being a part of something so very personal to them, they've made me feel like part of the family during the past twenty-four hours.

"Do you remember that?" Ford can barely get the words out he's laughing so hard.

"Fuck. I got in so much trouble for that one," Callahan says, holding the picture and staring at it.

"You?" Ledger all but spits his beer out. "You're the one who poured the bleach on the lawn and spelled D-I-C-K, and I'm the one who got in trouble when I was just trying to clean it up."

"I told you to use spray paint to hide it," Callahan says. "Works like a charm."

"Fucker," Ledger says but laughs.

There is an ease between the three of them that is so inviting, so welcoming, I step into the open doorway and simply smile.

Callahan notices me and motions for me to sit beside him.

"C'mon, Sutton," Ledger says when he notices his brother looking my way. "I'm certain we're getting to some really embarrassing pictures of Callahan when we were little."

"Bowl haircuts and all," Ford says.

"Dude, if I had one then you had one," Callahan says.

"Blackmail material?" I ask as I move toward the table. "Yes, please." I yelp when I go to sit down and Callahan grabs me by the waist, pulling me to sit on his lap.

He kisses my cheek as he wraps his arms around me.

Effortless.

That's what this is between us and it still astounds me every time we're together. How easy this love we have is. We've spent a month working in Manhattan, three months at an old property in Napa that needed some work, and then back in Manhattan again . . . and while that time included long, hard hours of work, the time between was incredible. Laughter and love making and comfortable silence interspersed with more laughter.

For a man who didn't think he knew how to love, he's shown me daily how cherished I am, how important and vital I am to him. He's shown me how it is to be loved by someone's whole heart.

"I'm glad you're here," Callahan murmurs in my ear, giving a perfect example to illustrate my thoughts.

"I am too."

"See? Bowl cuts," Ford says, sliding a picture in front of me that has me laughing so hard it brings tears to my eyes.

They show me pictures, one after another. They share pieces of their life with me, stories, and images of their father I never met, but who still remains present. We laugh. Eyes water. Glances of brotherly love are exchanged.

"See? I told you that you picked the right brother," Callahan says after he holds up a picture of them as teenagers. Callahan has his shirt off and is flexing.

"Let me see that." I take the picture and hold it closer to my face. "You sure that's you? I'm pretty sure that's Ford," I tease.

Ford laughs and high-fives me.

But it's only when I look back toward Callahan does the laughter fade from my lips. "What is it?" I ask suddenly at the bittersweet look on his face.

I follow his gaze to the photograph that was apparently stuck to the back of the muscle pose one, and my heart leaps into my throat.

The image is faded and worn at the edges. The color is washed out in several spots. But as Callahan lifts it off the table, there is absolutely no mistaking what the image is of or where it was taken.

A young Maxton Sharpe is standing on a sandy bluff, the sun is overhead, and a peculiar yet unmistakable stack of rocks is to his right. His hair is blowing in the breeze, his smile mesmerized, as he looks over to the woman beside him. She's in a conservative sundress with a stylish hat on her head and the same adoring look on her face.

293

"Do you know where this is?" Callahan whispers, his eyes swimming with tears when he looks up from the image of his mom and dad.

I nod, my words escaping me and my own eyes filling with tears. "I do," I finally whisper.

It is the bluff in the Virgin Islands. The same one Callahan took me to on our last night together where we swayed in the hammock, sipped wine, and said a silent goodbye to each other.

"He was there. *He remembered.*" And when Callahan closes his eyes and exhales a shaky sigh, I can only fathom how much this picture means to him.

His dad had remembered the beach. The promise to his mom. *It was all real.* Not something the dementia stole and warped. It was one last truth his father shared with his son that Callahan could hold on to when he was gone.

The deal for the resort, the reasons he let his father sign the deal, and the reason we met, all were valid.

"He was right," Callahan whispers as he slides the picture across the table to his brothers. "He remembered."

Callahan

"I don't know where your head is, but if it's anywhere near where I think it is, you might want this."

"Want what?" I look over to where he's holding a black velvet box.

"Ford and I agreed that you should have this."

"Ledge. What . . ." I open the box and stare. Nestled within the cushioned insides is an oval cut solitaire set in place by an intricate band. Our mother's engagement ring. I look up at my brother and then back to the ring. "I don't know what to say."

"There's nothing to say." His smile is as kind as the hand he pats on my back with before walking out and leaving me staring at something that was so incredibly special to my mom.

Just as Sutton is to me.

The sun is slowly rising over the Atlantic. Its warm rays fill the room we're staying in at the Sag Harbor house. I stare at the ceiling and take in everything that has happened in the last forty-eight hours.

The ring. The picture. I mean . . . I feel like my dad is here, speaking to me, getting the last laugh out of everything.

Maybe one day you'll fall in love and bring her to this place too, Callahan. Your mother would love that.

If he only knew.

Then again, I have a feeling he does. And a part of me wonders if he's had a hand in all of this somehow—the reconciliation with my brothers, finding my place in the company and making it my own. *And in finding Sutton.*

With a soft smile on my lips, I turn on my side. She's lying beside me, her dark hair fanned out on the white sheets and her unmistakable natural beauty on display.

How did I get so fucking lucky?

Two years ago, I was a man drowning in misdirection, one who was pissed off at the world. And now . . . now, there's the woman beside me.

Sutton's eyes flutter open and a slow, sleepy smile lights up her beautiful face. "Morning."

"Hi."

"You're staring at me," she says and when she brings a hand up to cover her face, I reach out to stop her.

"Don't. You're beautiful."

Yes. I'm that sap now. The ones I used to make fun of, but I'm perfectly fucking okay with it, because look what I get out of it. *Her.*

"Why do you look so intense this early in the morning?" she asks.

"I'm just thinking."

"About all the stuff yesterday?" She reaches out and runs a hand over my bicep before letting it rest there.

"That and some other things."

"Like?"

"You."

"Me?" she says through a laugh.

I nod, nerves suddenly rattling around. "Mm-hmm. About how you deserve a big fancy proposal. One filled with a million flowers and balloons and the fanciest of everything from our bluff in the Virgin Islands." There is shock on her face, but rest assured, I'm just as surprised by my own words. "But to be honest, I don't want to wait for that. I'm an impatient man, and while I could take the time to set that all up with some fancy coordinator, I don't want to waste another day. I want to ask you now. In the house I spent summers in, down the hall from the room I last saw my mother in, in a place I've only ever known happiness."

"You do, do you?" she says calmly, her eyes owning mine, as I too, try to wrap my head around what the fuck I'm doing.

But I know.

I think deep down I've always known.

Collins is the one. *She always has been.*

"*I do.* It's as simple as that. I want to marry you, Sutton Pierce. And I will give you a lifetime of the luxuries you deserve, of all the sexy panties you want, but all I have to offer you in return is *me.* The me who's stubborn and defiant and sometimes a little unyielding. The same me who promises to love you with all my heart." I chuckle. "Not that I ever had an option when it came to you."

"You're being serious, aren't you?" she asks, suddenly realizing that I'm not playing around.

I shift and sit up in bed. "It's funny how that happens—how *we* happened. One day you weren't a thought on my radar, and the next thing you were the only thing I could think about. And you still are, Collins." I reach behind me to the nightstand drawer and pull out the box Ledger handed me yesterday. "So yes, you deserve to be in a fancy dress instead of naked under covers. Yes, you deserve to be wined and dined before being asked instead of on an empty stomach. Yes, you deserve the world instead of sitting in a bed at seven in the morning, staring wide-eyed at me."

"It's perfect. You're perfect." She presses a kiss to my lips. "This—you—us—is all I've ever wanted. All I've ever needed. All the fancy stuff doesn't matter, Callahan, because at the end of the day, it comes down to you and me and the naked truth that I love you with all my heart and would be honored to be your wife and share your family with you."

"You will? You would?" I stutter the questions out like a nervous schoolboy because, while I didn't worry about what her answer would be, I still needed to hear it. Still needed to know.

"I will and I would," she says shifting in the bed to sit up, her cross-legged knees hitting mine as the sun lights up her face.

I open the box and pull the ring out. "I've only ever loved two women in my life, Sutton, you and my mother. It's only fitting that you wear what was once hers. What was once a symbol of an unbreakable love across time, beyond sickness, and even after death."

"It's beautiful," she says, the first tear sliding over and down her cheek.

"Will you marry me?"

She leans forward and kisses me tenderly, her hands framing my face before leaning back and looking in my eyes. "Yes. A million times . . . yes."

Did you enjoy Callahan and Sutton's journey toward their happily ever after? Are you intrigued by both Ledger and Ford and want to find out more about them? There are two books remaining in the S.I.N. series. (The books can be read in any order). You can find them here:
www.kbromberg.com/books/sin-series

On One Condition
Final Proposal

Are you looking for another wealthy book boyfriends to warm your metaphorical bed? Why not get acquainted these other K. Bromberg's heroes:

Faking It (standalone, billionaire hero, fake dating, forced proximity): After a little white lie spirals out of control, billionaire Zane Phillips hires Harlow Nicks to play his girlfriend to promote his new dating website. The problem? She doesn't exactly like him. But a job is a job and she has bills to pay. But as the miles unfurl, so does their passion . . . and if Harlow's not careful, she might end up believing that fairytales really do come true. Find Faking It at www.kbromberg.com/books/standalone-novels/faking-it

Wicked Ways Duet: This two book series (Resist, Reveal) will hit all your buttons. Taboo/Forbidden Romance. Enemies to Lovers. Strong Alpha. A hint of suspense. Vaughn and Ryker are a battle of wills from the start but will win each other's hearts in the end. Find out more about the Wicked Ways duet at www.kbromberg.com/books/wicked-ways

Play Hard Series: Four sisters try to save their family's sports management agency, and in the process, they find their soulmates. Tropes used are sports romance (each book deals with a different sport), military romance, enemies to lovers, forced proximity, British hero, childhood crush . . . and on and on. Each book focuses on a different set of tropes. Find out which ones at www.kbromberg.com/books/play-hard-series.

ABOUT THE AUTHOR

New York Times Bestselling author K. Bromberg writes contemporary romance novels that contain a mixture of sweet, emotional, a whole lot of sexy, and a little bit of real. She likes to write strong heroines and damaged heroes who we love to hate but can't help to love.

A mom of three, she plots her novels in between school runs and soccer practices, more often than not with her laptop in tow and her mind scattered in too many different directions.

Since publishing her first book on a whim in 2013, Kristy has sold over two million copies of her books across twenty different countries and has landed on the *New York Times, USA Today,* and *Wall Street Journal* Bestsellers lists over thirty times. Her Driven trilogy (*Driven, Fueled,* and *Crashed*) has been adapted for film and is available on the streaming platform Passionflix as well as Amazon.

You can find out more about him or chat with Kristy on any of her social media accounts. The easiest way to stay up to date on new releases and upcoming novels is to sign up for her newsletter or follow her on Bookbub.

Made in United States
Orlando, FL
29 May 2022

18293775R00170